On Writers & Writing

By Helen Sheehy and Leslie Stainton

Published by Tide-mark Press Ltd.

 New Moon First Quarter Full Moon Last Quarter

Constantin Stanislavski
January 5, 1863* – August 7, 1938

When Stanislavski was a boy, the smell of
the gas lights in the theatre filled him with
strong, dizzying emotions, and all of his
spare time, he recalled, "was devoted to the
theatre." The son of a wealthy Moscow
merchant, Stanislavski spent his youth in a
peaceful Russia. "We drank from the full cup
of life," he said.

One of his earliest memories was of acting
"Winter" in a family performance. "They put
a lighted candle in front of me, hidden in
brushwood, to represent a bonfire," he wrote,
"and gave me a stick which I was to pretend
to put into it." This seemed absurd to him.
"As soon as the curtains opened for the
encore I stretched out my hand with the stick towards the fire….It seemed to me
that this was a completely natural and logical action, one with thought behind it."
Of course, the stick burst into flame along with the cotton wool "snow" that covered
the set.

For the rest of his life, Stanislavski searched for naturalness and truth in acting. He
published his findings in *My Life in Art, An Actor Prepares, Building a Character,* and
Creating a Role. Ironically, the Moscow Art Theatre, which he co-founded, never
produced a great acting genius, and Stanislavski himself lacked a natural gift for
acting. "I envied great actors like Salvini, Duse, and Yermolova," he wrote, " and I
asked them in my thought what they did in order to rise freely to the highest point of
their passion."

Stanislavski devised exercises and techniques to stimulate the creative imagination of
the actor, but he also believed that "nine tenths of the labor of an actor…lies in
beginning to feel the role spiritually." His books contributed immeasurably to the art
of acting, but they could not replace what Stanislavski called the "sphere of living
tradition." He advised that the "true foundation of the art of the theatre…can only be
passed from hand to hand."

Stanislavski survived cataclysmic changes in Russia. He never wavered in his effort to
turn his life and his emotions into art. He compared himself to a prospector who had
to wash tons of sand and stones to discover one streak of gold. "And like the gold-
seeker," he wrote, "I cannot will to my heirs my labors, my quests, my losses, my joys
and my disappointment, but only the few grains of gold that it has taken me all my life
to find."

*Julian Calendar

Sunday
30

Monday
31

Tuesday
1

Catherine Drinker Bowen, b. 1897   New Year's Day

Wednesday
2

Thursday
3

J.R.R. Tolkien, b. 1892

Friday
4

 Saturday
5

Constantin Stanislavski, b. (Julian Calendar) 1863

December 2001						
S	M	T	W	T	F	S
						1
2	3	4	5	6	7	8
9	10	11	12	13	14	15
16	17	18	19	20	21	22
23	24	25	26	27	28	29
30	31					

December 2001/ January 2002

January						
S	M	T	W	T	F	S
		1	2	3	4	5
6	7	8	9	10	11	12
13	14	15	16	17	18	19
20	21	22	23	24	25	26
27	28	29	30	31		

Sunday

6

Epiphany, Three Kings Day   *Carl Sandburg, b. 1878*

Monday

7

Zora Neale Hurston, b. 1891

Tuesday

8

Wilkie Collins, b. 1824   Baltasar Gracián, b. 1601

Wednesday

9

Simone de Beauvoir, b. 1908

Thursday

10

Robinson Jeffers, b. 1887

Friday

11

Eva Le Gallienne, b. 1899   Jack London, b. 1876   Alan Paton, b. 1903

Saturday

12

January						
S	M	T	W	T	F	S
		1	2	3	4	5
6	7	8	9	10	11	12
13	14	15	16	17	18	19
20	21	22	23	24	25	26
27	28	29	30	31		

January
2002

February						
S	M	T	W	T	F	S
					1	2
3	4	5	6	7	8	9
10	11	12	13	14	15	16
17	18	19	20	21	22	23
24	25	26	27	28		

Baltasar Gracián
January 8, 1601 – December 6, 1658

Three hundred years before Ann Landers, a little-known Jesuit priest from Aragón had this to say to those seeking to improve themselves: "Know when to put something aside. One of life's great lessons lies in knowing how to refuse." "Know how to contradict. It is a great way to provoke others." "Don't be obsessed with the latest." "Associate with those you can learn from."

And more. Baltasar Gracián, a worldly priest with an abiding contempt for human folly, left 300 such gems in his timeless compendium of moral and practical advice, *The Art of Worldly Wisdom: A Pocket Oracle.* "The reader today who faithfully follows its precepts," writes the author Gail Godwin, "will never make a fool of himself or herself and may even go on to become useful and wise."

Like Machiavelli's *The Prince* and Sun-Tzu's *The Art of War*, with which it is often compared, Gracián's *Oracle* draws insights on the art of living from careful observation of everyday behavior.

He was born in the first year of the 17th century, a time of social turbulence and political decline in Spain. Gracián harbored no illusions about the moral state of his compatriots. "It takes more to make one sage today than it did to make the seven of Greece," he declared.

In his youth he studied philosophy and letters. At 18, he entered a Jesuit order, where he worked variously as a preacher, professor, administrator, and confessor. He served briefly as chaplain to the royal armies battling the French.

Through a wealthy friend and protector, Gracián gained access to one of most extensive private collections of books, manuscripts, and paintings in Aragón—a vital resource for an inveterate writer who yearned to be "vulgar in nothing."

Besides the *Oracle*, Gracián wrote a number of treatises; one satirical novel; and *El discreto* (1646), a manual on gentlemanly behavior in the tradition of Castiglione's *Courtier*. Because his Jesuit order forbade him to publish without permission, Gracián issued much of his work under a pseudonym.

Ultimately, the order could not tolerate his disobedience and exiled Gracián to a country town, where he remained until his death, under close watch lest he write anything against the Jesuits. The ultimate pragmatist, Gracián took his punishment in stride. "I am prohibited from publishing, and have no lack of envious people," he wrote in 1653. "But I bear it all patiently, and am still able to eat lunch and dinner, to sleep, etc."

Compton Mackenzie
January 17, 1883 – November 30, 1972

His friend D. H. Lawrence called Compton Mackenzie "The Man Who Loved Islands," and it was true. Mackenzie lived on many islands during his long and prolific existence: Capri, the Channel Islands, the Outer Hebrides. Island life, he believed, "restores human dignity. The individual is not overwhelmed by his own unimportance. This is particularly beneficent for the artist, who requires the solitude necessary to make him feel that the work he is producing today is not a futile drop in an ocean of human endeavor."

The oldest son of two of the most successful actors of the Victorian age, Mackenzie claimed an artist's life as his birthright. By 13, he'd read "every play of major and minor importance written and produced by the year 1830," or so he claimed. At Oxford, where the task of turning in weekly essays gave him the discipline a writer needs, he founded a literary review, wrote poetry, and composed his first play. He later said he "always meant to be a playwright."

But novels were his mainstay. In all, Mackenzie produced some 100 books, nearly half of which are novels. He took Britain by storm with his first work of fiction, *The Passionate Elopement* (1911), a lively account of debaucheries at an 18th-century spa. His second novel, *Carnival* (1912), drew praise from Yeats, J. M. Barrie, and Henry James. F. Scott Fitzgerald admitted writing *This Side of Paradise* under the spell of Mackenzie's best-selling third novel, *Sinister Street*.

Mackenzie also wrote essays, memoirs, and criticism. He often wrote merely to pay the bills generated by his luxurious lifestyle. (His innumerable purchases include two small islands.) Mackenzie regarded his vocation as "day-to-day-work," to be carried out "whether or not he had something worthwhile to say."

He preferred to write late at night, accompanied by chamber music on the gramophone. So great was Mackenzie's attachment to recorded music, in fact, that he founded the magazine *Gramophone*.

He married three times, fought in World War I, served as rector of Glasgow University, and embraced Roman Catholicism. At 89, he was still hard at work, having already produced ten volumes of autobiography. Nearly blind, he steered his pen across the page with tightly drawn wires.

Mackenzie died, appropriately for the devout Scotsman he was, on St. Andrew's Day, and is buried on Barra, one of the southernmost islands of the Outer Hebrides.

 *Sunday*
13
Horatio Alger, Jr., b. 1832

Monday
14

Yukio Mishima, b. 1925

Tuesday
15

Osip Mandelstam, b. 1891   Molière, b. 1622

Wednesday
16

Thursday
17

Charles Brockden Brown, b. 1771
Anne Brontë, b. 1820   Don Pedro Calderón de la Barca, b. 1600   Compton Mackenzie, b. 1883

Friday
18

A. A. Milne, b. 1882   Peter Mark Roget, b. 1779

Saturday
19
Richard Le Gallienne, b. 1866

January						
S	M	T	W	T	F	S
	1	2	3	4	5	
6	7	8	9	10	11	12
13	14	15	16	17	18	19
20	21	22	23	24	25	26
27	28	29	30	31		

January
2002

February						
S	M	T	W	T	F	S
					1	2
3	4	5	6	7	8	9
10	11	12	13	14	15	16
17	18	19	20	21	22	23
24	25	26	27	28		

Sunday
20
Edgar Allan Poe, b. 1809

Monday
21

Martin Luther King, Jr. Day

Tuesday
22

George Gordon, Lord Byron, b. 1788   August Strindberg, b. 1849

Wednesday
23

Thursday
24

Edith Wharton, b. 1862   William Congreve, b. 1670

Friday
25

W. Somerset Maugham, b. 1874   Virginia Woolf, b. 1882

Saturday
26

January						
S	M	T	W	T	F	S
		1	2	3	4	5
6	7	8	9	10	11	12
13	14	15	16	17	18	19
20	21	22	23	24	25	26
27	28	29	30	31		

January
2002

February						
S	M	T	W	T	F	S
					1	2
3	4	5	6	7	8	9
10	11	12	13	14	15	16
17	18	19	20	21	22	23
24	25	26	27	28		

August Strindberg
January 22, 1849 – May 14, 1912

Ibsen put Strindberg's portrait on the wall of his study. "He is my mortal enemy and shall hang there and watch while I write," Ibsen said. Actually, as Ibsen biographer Michael Meyer points out, Strindberg was Ibsen's successor and "wrote of sex with a frankness which Ibsen, being Ibsen, could not match." Both authors wrestled with the complexities of the human soul, and deciding which dramatist is greater is "like arguing whether Bach is superior to Beethoven," writes Meyer.

Of the two dramatists, Strindberg was the most troubled and most difficult. As a boy growing up in Stockholm, Sweden, Strindberg thought of family life as a prison. His older brother Axel recalled that the family never suspected that golden-haired August was a genius. "He was extremely shy," Axel said, "so shy with us brothers that he changed his underwear in a closet!"

As a teenager, Strindberg "gulped down" Shakespeare. He attended the University of Uppsala, but never got a degree. He called himself the "son of a servant" and felt out of place in the academic world. For a time he considered becoming an actor or a doctor, but failed his tryout at the Royal Theatre and flunked chemistry at the University of Uppsala. On the same day that he failed his theatre audition, Strindberg began writing his first play. In 1872, he began meeting with other young artists at the Red Room in Berns' Restaurant in Stockholm, and he also met his first wife, a beautiful baroness. Five years later, he published his first novel, *The Red Room*, a satire about Stockholm society.

In his work, he was remarkably frank about his personal life. *The Confession of a Fool,* a book about his first marriage, used all the resources of psychology, he said, such as "suggestion, thought-reading, the methods of psychic torture—I will not neglect even the old tried tricks of burglary, theft, interception of letters, lying, forged signatures; in a word investigate everything."

Strindberg's work anticipated the alienation and disorientation of modern life. His plays in the 1880s, including *The Father, Miss Julie*, and *The Stronger*, followed by *A Dream Play* in 1902 and *The Ghost Sonata* in 1907 helped shape the modern theatre. "My souls (characters) are conglomerations of past and present cultures," he wrote, "bits out of books and newspapers, pieces of human beings, torn-off shreds of holiday clothes that have become rags, exactly as the human soul is put together."

John O'Hara
January 31, 1905 – April 11, 1970

John O'Hara wrote his own epitaph, which is engraved on his tombstone in Princeton, New Jersey: "Better than anyone else, he told the truth about his time, the first half of the twentieth century. He was a professional. He wrote honestly and well."

The arrogance of that "anyone else" enraged O'Hara's critics. Still, great writers, like great actors and athletes, have to believe in themselves, and O'Hara had an astonishing belief in his own talent.

Born in Pottsville, Pennsylvania (which he transformed into the fictional world of Gibbsville), O'Hara was raised in affluence. At four, he taught himself to read from newspaper headlines, and he was soon reading Booth Tarkington and F. Scott Fitzgerald. He became "fascinated by the small-town boy in the Ivy League world." Later, he quipped that he loved Fitzgerald's *This Side of Paradise* so much that he slept with it. After the death of his surgeon father, O'Hara couldn't afford his dream of going to Yale and instead traveled and worked at a series of menial jobs. Dreaming of becoming a writer, he moved to New York and wrote for various newspapers. In 1928 he sold his first story to *The New Yorker,* and six years later he published his first novel, *Appointment in Samarra.*

Most of O'Hara's 31 novels, including *Butterfield 8, Pal Joey, Ten North Frederick*, as well as his short story collections, were best-sellers. Readers identified with his social-climbing characters obsessed with sex, money, and status and loved his page-turning plots, flat, transparent prose, and realistic dialogue. Throughout his career, though, O'Hara never won the critical acclaim that he thought he deserved. "Mr. O'Hara can write like a streak," wrote Clifton Fadiman, "but he just won't think, or at any rate he won't think in his novels."

O'Hara wrote mostly at night in a well-organized study that he called his "laboratory." One of his lab experiments was to think about two faces that he had seen in a restaurant or on an airplane. "I let them do small talk for a page or two," he wrote, "and pretty soon they begin to come to life. They do so entirely through dialog…. A fine novel can be written about any two people in the world—by a first rate novelist."

His friends often found his arrogant, thin-skinned behavior trying and second-rate, but even his enemies recognized his consummate professionalism. "O'Hara came to write as naturally as he breathed," wrote Brendan Gill, "and for the same reason: it kept him alive."

Sunday

27

Lewis Carroll, b. 1832

Monday

28

Sidonie-Gabrielle Colette, b. 1873

Tuesday

29

Thomas Paine, b. 1737   *Anton Chekhov, b. 1860*

Wednesday

30

Richard Brautigan, b. 1935

Thursday

31

John O'Hara, b. 1905

Friday

1

Saturday

2

Ayn Rand, b. 1905   *James Joyce, b. 1882*   Ground Hog Day

January						
S	M	T	W	T	F	S
	1	2	3	4	5	
6	7	8	9	10	11	12
13	14	15	16	17	18	19
20	21	22	23	24	25	26
27	28	29	30	31		

January/
February
2002

February						
S	M	T	W	T	F	S
					1	2
3	4	5	6	7	8	9
10	11	12	13	14	15	16
17	18	19	20	21	22	23
24	25	26	27	28		

Sunday

3

Gertrude Stein, b. 1874   Sidney Lanier, b. 1842

Monday

4

Tuesday

5

Wednesday

6

Thursday

7

Charles Dickens, b. 1812   Laura Ingalls Wilder, b. 1867

Friday

8

Jules Verne, b. 1828   Kate Chopin, b. 1850   Elizabeth Bishop, b. 1911

Saturday

9

Amy Lowell, b. 1874   Brendan Behan, b. 1923

February						
S	M	T	W	T	F	S
					1	2
3	4	5	6	7	8	9
10	11	12	13	14	15	16
17	18	19	20	21	22	23
24	25	26	27	28		

February
2002

March						
S	M	T	W	T	F	S
					1	2
3	4	5	6	7	8	9
10	11	12	13	14	15	16
17	18	19	20	21	22	23
24	25	26	27	28	29	30
31						

Brendan Behan

February 9, 1923 – March 20, 1964

Life may have been a dream for Calderón. For Brendan Behan, it was merely "a bloody sight better than death any day of the week."

Behan harbored few illusions about anything. His father was in jail, serving a sentence for Irish Republican Army activities, when Brendan was born. Brendan himself joined the IRA in his teens, and at 16 was arrested in

Brendan Behan (l) with Jackie Gleason

Liverpool for possession of explosives and sent to an English reform school. His years there inspired the autobiographical *Borstal Boy* (1958), Behan's best nondramatic work.

He returned to his native Dublin in 1942 and promptly got into a drunken shoot-out with police that led to a 14-year prison sentence; it was commuted in 1946. While in jail, Behan perfected Gaelic. In 1948 he was sentenced to the first of many short jail terms for drunkenness (he'd begun drinking at age eight).

If his problems were prodigious, so was his talent. He came from a musical family—his mother sang rebel songs, and his uncle wrote the Irish national anthem. In his late twenties, Behan himself began singing songs on an Irish radio program. He also wrote radio scripts and short stories and published a column in the *Irish Press*.

His reputation rests chiefly on two plays, *The Quare Fellow* (1954), set in an Irish prison on the eve of an execution, and *The Hostage* (1958), originally written in Gaelic, about a Cockney soldier who is held as a hostage in reprisal for an IRA man about to be hanged. In both plays, Behan blends bawdy humor with genuine pathos to forge a savage commentary on human society.

Of *The Hostage*, critic Walter Kerr wrote, "If you can imagine a bad dream that is a good dream, you will have come close to the *pot au feu* that Mr. Behan has stirred with a witch's ladle and then slopped, with nightmare gaiety, all over the stage."

The plays were produced during the most productive period in Behan's life, his marriage to painter Beatrice ffrench-Salkeld, who recognized her husband's weaknesses and tried vainly to help him.

Behan wrote his last works—a play, a novel, and a series of memoirs—largely by dictation into a tape recorder. He died in 1964, a few months after the birth of his daughter.

"The bells of hell / Go ting-a-ling-a-ling / For you but not for me," he had written in *The Hostage*. "/ Oh death where is thy / Sting-a-ling-a-ling / Or grave thy victory?"

Henry Adams
February 16, 1838 – March 27, 1918

The great-grandson of John Adams, second
president of the United States; grandson of
John Quincy Adams, sixth president; and son
of Charles Francis Adams, a Massachusetts
statesman, editor of ancestral papers, and
eventual minister to Great Britain, Henry
Adams was, as he later phrased it, "distinctly
branded." The Adams family legacy in
politics and letters weighed heavily on
"ten pounds of unconscious babyhood,"
Henry wrote.

Adams resisted the weight of tradition. He
scorned primary school, chafed at the
formality of Harvard, and abandoned plans
to study law at the University of Berlin when
he found the German language too hard.

He tried his hand at politics, journalism, and teaching. During a stint as a professor of
medieval history at Harvard (a position for which he lacked formal credentials),
Adams revealed his true priorities by writing letters to friends during faculty meetings.

Having "failed" (his word) to forge a conventional career, Adams became a lifelong
student and wanderer, addicted to the "accidental education" that travel provides.

He also wrote. Adams is one of our finest travel writers and greatest historians. His
prodigious output includes essays, biographies, a nine-volume history of the United
States under Jefferson and Madison, and the memoirs of the last queen of Tahiti.

Adams also produced two novels, *Democracy: An American Novel* (1880) and *Esther*
(1884). The former, a satire of the American political system that exposes the corruption then rampant in Washington, D.C., anticipates Joe Klein by a century. Like Klein,
Adams published his work anonymously.

But he is best known for two works: *Mont-Saint-Michel and Chartres* (1904) and *The
Education of Henry Adams: An Autobiography* (1907).

Of the bantering, informal, evocative *Mont-Saint-Michel*, a reflection of 13th-century
France as written by an old uncle for his nieces, Adams claimed it was "my talk, for I
deny that it is a book."

Of *The Education*, he said it was his attempt to "fix for a familiar moment a necessary
sequence of human movement." Nominally an autobiography, Adams's *Education* is
at once a memoir and a panoramic representation of American history as seen by one
man in his time.

The book, which won a posthumous Pulitzer, triumphed where Adams himself did not
always. His only marriage ended in 1885 when his wife committed suicide. Adams
never recovered from the incident (he does not mention it in his autobiography). He
died in 1918 and is buried in the Washington he both loathed and loved, beneath a
melancholy, inscrutable statue, which he had years earlier commissioned to adorn his
wife's grave.

Sunday
10
Bertolt Brecht, b. 1898   *Boris Pasternak, b. 1890*

Monday
11

 ## Tuesday
12

Lunar New Year, Year of the Horse
Shrove Tuesday
Charles Darwin, b. 1809   Abraham Lincoln, born 1809

Wednesday
13

Georges Simenon, b. 1903   Ash Wednesday

Thursday
14

St. Valentine's Day

Friday
15

Saturday
16
Henry Adams, b. 1838

February

S	M	T	W	T	F	S
					1	2
3	4	5	6	7	8	9
10	11	12	13	14	15	16
17	18	19	20	21	22	23
24	25	26	27	28		

February
2002

March

S	M	T	W	T	F	S
					1	2
3	4	5	6	7	8	9
10	11	12	13	14	15	16
17	18	19	20	21	22	23
24	25	26	27	28	29	30
31						

Sunday
17

Monday
18

Presidents' Day   *Nikos Kazantzakis, b. 1883   Sholom Aleichem, b. 1859*

Tuesday
19

Carson McCullers, b. 1917

Wednesday
20

Thursday
21

W.H. Auden, b. 1907   Anaïs Nin, b. 1903

Friday
22

Jane Bowles, b. 1917
George Washington, born 1732   *Meridel LeSueur, b. 1900   Edna St. Vincent Millay, b. 1892*

Saturday
23
W.E.B. Du Bois, b. 1868   Samuel Pepys, b. 1633

February

S	M	T	W	T	F	S
					1	2
3	4	5	6	7	8	9
10	11	12	13	14	15	16
17	18	19	20	21	22	23
24	25	26	27	28		

February
2002

March

S	M	T	W	T	F	S
					1	2
3	4	5	6	7	8	9
10	11	12	13	14	15	16
17	18	19	20	21	22	23
24	25	26	27	28	29	30
31						

Meridel LeSueur
February 22, 1900 – November 14, 1996

Meridel LeSueur was a child when her
mother left LeSueur's alcoholic, abusive
father and moved to Oklahoma, effectively
kidnapping LeSueur and her three siblings.

It was from her Native American neighbors
in Oklahoma that LeSueur first learned the
secrets of domestic life. Hidden under the
table during quilting sessions, LeSueur later
recalled, "I listened while the quilters talked
about the women in their families.... They
spoke of the women hidden in attics, spare
rooms, drinking Lydia Pinkham's medicine
—opium—or taking laudanum. I learned that
in every home there was a woman unknown."

LeSueur grew up to write about those women in stories and articles, many of which
were subsequently published in the 1982 Feminist Press compilation of LeSueur's
works, *Ripening*. "I felt that I was not only writing my own deep roots, but the deeper
life of all women," LeSueur said of her early years as an author. "To tell how we
suffered, how we were destroyed, macerated, ground out."

Her mother became a political radical (at 75, Marian LeSueur ran for the U. S. Senate
on the Progressive Party ticket), and Meridel followed in her footsteps. For a time, she
pursued an acting career. She got bit parts in Hollywood, but was told if she wanted a
contract, she had to fix her nose ("you look Jewish or Indian"). LeSueur refused and
turned to writing, her "passional" work. She rejoined her family in the Midwest. It
was the start of the Depression; by then LeSueur had two daughters, whom she raised
largely by herself.

The Depression reinforced her commitment to the Left and in dozens of short stories,
newspaper articles, poems, and books about everyday Americans, LeSueur voiced her
commitment to a new political and cultural reality.

Eventually she joined the Communist Party. The F.B.I. kept tabs on her and when she
tried to teach a correspondence course, the bureau hounded her students until most of
them quit. LeSueur herself was blacklisted; her work vanished from public sight.

A woman of many opinions, she understood her craft. "The plotted book with the hero
and heroine is an old-fashioned form," she said. "It's like capitalism, the goods
distributed to a few favored players."

In the 1970s, LeSueur was rediscovered and enjoyed something of a revival. At 84, a
decade before her death, she was still working, "getting in my crop before frost," she
said. "It's my life's crop I've planted, now I have to harvest it."

Ralph Ellison
March 1, 1914 – April 16, 1994

He wrote the first lines of his classic
novel, *Invisible Man*, sitting in an old
barn looking out on the mountains of
Vermont. After he wrote the first
sentence, he almost destroyed what he
had written, but then he heard a voice in
his head—the voice of a "blackface
comedian," he said, "bragging on the
stage of Harlem's Apollo Theatre to the
effect that each generation of his family
was becoming so progressively black of
complexion that no one, not even its
own mother, had ever been able to see
the two-year-old baby."

Ralph Ellison (r) with John Cheever

Ellison spent seven years writing *Invisible Man* and it was published in 1952. The
story of a nameless young black man's struggle against segregation, a young man who
becomes representative of all races, won the National Book Award and critical and
popular acclaim. Harold Bloom called the narrator the "only authentic American,
black or white, because he follows the American Religion, which is Emersonian
Self-Reliance."

In fact, Ellison was named Ralph Waldo after Emerson, the New England essayist.
Born in Oklahoma, Ellison was only three when his father died. He was raised by his
loving mother Ida, who surrounded the boy with books and music. Ellison played the
trumpet, met blues singers and musicians and he "heard the Blues sung and played all
my life, and an inescapable line was to be heard any day as I made my visits to back
alley joints and houses as a delivery boy: If you don't believe I'm sinking—Look
what a hole I'm in…"

His mother encouraged him to become a band leader like Duke Ellington, and Ellison
studied musical composition at Tuskegee Institute in Alabama. Ellison then decided to
move to New York and take his chances there. After meeting Langston Hughes and
Richard Wright, who encouraged him, Ellison worked on the Federal Writers Project
and devoted himself to writing. His work was also shaped by his reading of T.S. Eliot
and Ernest Hemingway; he studied Hemingway's dispatches from the Spanish Civil
War for "style as well as for information." During World War II, Ellison served as a
cook in the Merchant Marine. After the war, he began writing *Invisible Man.*

Unlike Hemingway, Ellison never exiled himself from America. "I am too vindictively
American," Ellison said, "too full of hate for the hateful aspects of this country, and
too possessed by the things I love here, to be too long away."

Sunday
24

Rosalía de Castro, b. 1837

Monday
25

Carlo Goldoni, b. 1707

Tuesday
26

Christopher Marlowe, b. 1564   Victor Hugo, b. 1802   Purim begins at sunset

Wednesday
27

Henry Wadsworth Longfellow, b. 1807   John Steinbeck, b. 1902

Thursday
28

Michel de Montaigne, b. 1533   Ben Hecht, b. 1879

Friday
1

Ralph Ellison, b. 1914   Robert Lowell, b. 1917

Saturday
2

Theodore Seuss Geisel (Dr. Seuss), b. 1904   Camille Desmoulins, b. 1760

February						
S	M	T	W	T	F	S
					1	2
3	4	5	6	7	8	9
10	11	12	13	14	15	16
17	18	19	20	21	22	23
24	25	26	27	28		

February/
March
2002

March						
S	M	T	W	T	F	S
					1	2
3	4	5	6	7	8	9
10	11	12	13	14	15	16
17	18	19	20	21	22	23
24	25	26	27	28	29	30
31						

Sunday
3
William Godwin, b. 1756

Monday
4

Tuesday
5

Constance Fenimore Woolson, b. 1840

Wednesday
6

Thursday
7

Elizabeth Barrett Browning, b. 1806   Ring Lardner, b. 1885   Matilde Serao, b. 1857

Friday
8

Saturday
9
Vita Sackville-West, b. 1892

March						
S	M	T	W	T	F	S
					1	2
3	4	5	6	7	8	9
10	11	12	13	14	15	16
17	18	19	20	21	22	23
24	25	26	27	28	29	30
31						

March
2002

April						
S	M	T	W	T	F	S
	1	2	3	4	5	6
7	8	9	10	11	12	13
14	15	16	17	18	19	20
21	22	23	24	25	26	27
28	29	30				

William Godwin
March 3, 1756 – April 7, 1836

Born the seventh of 13 children (only six lived to be adults) in Wisbech, a boggy, damp, and dismal part of England, William Godwin survived parental neglect, including being "suckled by a hireling," and various childhood illnesses. He began reading at three. The precocious boy worried about what he should do "when I have read through all the books that have been written?"

In a career that spanned half a century, Godwin wrote almost 50 books, histories, memoirs, plays, essays, novels, pamphlets, even children's books, ensuring that he would never run out of reading material.

AUTHOR OF "THOUGHTS ON MAN."

Like his father, Godwin became a minister but, unable to reconcile his doubts with his faith, he left the ministry and turned to a literary career.

Struggling to earn his living as a writer in London, Godwin recalled, "for the most part I did not eat my dinner without previously carrying my watch or my books to the pawnbroker to enable me to eat." His 11th book, an *Inquiry Concerning the Principles of Political Justice* (1793)—which criticized aristocratic rule, defended liberalism, and introduced the ideas of the French Revolution to a British audience—brought him money and fame. After the success of *Political Justice*, William Hazlitt reported that Godwin "blazed as a sun in the firmament of reputation."

Pursued by several women, Godwin chose the brilliant Mary Wollstonecraft to be his wife. Wollstonecraft's manifesto, *A Vindication of the Rights of Women*, established her reputation and place in history. The two philosophers married in 1797, but that same year Mary died shortly after giving birth to their daughter—Mary Shelley, later the author of *Frankenstein*.

Hoping to "be made wise and more human by the contemplation of the memory of a beloved object," Godwin wrote in his study under Mary's portrait. In 1798, believing that biography should not be limited by the "factitious rules of decorum," Godwin published Mary's memoirs, which revealed her love affairs, suicide attempts, and the stark details of her agonizing death. Tory critics attacked the book, calling Mary a prostitute and Godwin her pimp.

Godwin told his friends after Mary's death that he would never be happy again. He remarried (a woman none of his friends liked), and through poverty, bankruptcy, and estrangement from his daughter when she eloped with Percy Bysshe Shelley, Godwin may not have been happy, but he never stopped writing. "Cough. Snow." are the last two words he wrote in a journal that he had kept continuously for 48 years.

Madame Louise d'Épinay
March 11, 1726 – April 17, 1783

Having just clapped eyes on a portrait of
Louise d'Épinay, her friend Denis Diderot
noted that it was an excellent likeness.
"Her mouth is slightly open: one sees her
breathe: and her eyes are filled with languor.
It is the very image of tenderness and
voluptuousness."

Madame d'Épinay herself was not so
complimentary. "I have a youthful look, but
without freshness: noble, gentle, lively, and
interesting," she wrote in one of her early
books.

Interesting and lively she was, especially in
her writings, among them her luminous
correspondence; her novel, or "pseudo-memoirs," *L'Histoire de Madame de
Montbrillant*; and her memories, in dialogue form, of the education she gave her
granddaughter, *Les Conversations d'Émilie*.

Saint-Beuve praised her for having captured the customs and conventions of 18th-
century France as no one else. "Madame d'Épinay's memoirs are not a book," he
proclaimed, "they are an epoch."

Told in childhood she was both inferior and ugly, she received the paltry education
reserved for girls at the time ("above all, we were never taught to think"). At 19, she
married a cousin, Denis-Joseph Lalive d'Épinay, a crude philanderer who promptly
infected Louise with venereal disease. They had one child before Louise demanded,
and was granted, a separation—along with the return of her dowry.

Liberated from Denis, Madame d'Épinay took the first of several lovers, had two
additional children, established a private theatre on her property, and became a noted
hostess to the eminent men and women of her day, including Jean-Jacques Rousseau,
who famously quarreled with d'Épinay and wrote of their breach in his *Confessions*.

Madame d'Épinay described her conversations with the literati of Paris as her
"university." Soon she was reading philosophy on her own and had embarked on an
epistolary novel.

But fiction was not her strength. It is in her memoirs and letters that d'Épinay reveals
herself as the quick-witted, resilient, intelligent woman she was. "A reputation as a
woman of sense and wit seems to me mere persiflage invented by men in revenge for
our usually having more attractive minds than they," she tells a correspondent. Later,
in the same letter: "Are you asleep? Wake up! I have finished my harangue."

Marcel Proust once imagined what it must have been like to move in d'Épinay's orbit.
He imagined the elevated conversation, the parlor games, the pursuit of work in the
morning, followed by lunch. "My mouth," he said, "waters for the life."

Sunday

10

Fanny Trollope, b. 1779   Mother's Day (U.K.)

Monday

11

Madame Louise d'Épinay, b. 1726

Tuesday

12

Jack Kerouac, b. 1922   *Gabriele D'Annunzio, b. 1863*

 Wednesday

13

Janet Flanner, b. 1892

Thursday

14

Albert Einstein, b. 1879

Friday

15

Lady Gregory, b. 1852   *Richard Ellmann, b. 1918*   Muharram, Islamic year 1423

Saturday

16

March						
S	M	T	W	T	F	S
					1	2
3	4	5	6	7	8	9
10	11	12	13	14	15	16
17	18	19	20	21	22	23
24	25	26	27	28	29	30
31						

March
2002

April						
S	M	T	W	T	F	S
	1	2	3	4	5	6
7	8	9	10	11	12	13
14	15	16	17	18	19	20
21	22	23	24	25	26	27
28	29	30				

Sunday
17
St. Patrick's Day   *Kate Greenaway, b. 1846   Paul Green, b. 1894*

Monday
18

Tuesday
19

Wednesday
20

Spring Equinox, 2:16 pm EST
Ovid, b. 43 B.C.   Henrik Ibsen, b. 1828   Friedrich Hölderlin, b. 1770   Nikolai Gogol, b. 1809

Thursday
21

Friday
22

Fannie Merritt Farmer, b. 1857

Saturday
23

March						
S	M	T	W	T	F	S
					1	2
3	4	5	6	7	8	9
10	11	12	13	14	15	16
17	18	19	20	21	22	23
24	25	26	27	28	29	30
31						

March
2002

April						
S	M	T	W	T	F	S
	1	2	3	4	5	6
7	8	9	10	11	12	13
14	15	16	17	18	19	20
21	22	23	24	25	26	27
28	29	30				

Olaudah Equiano
(Gustavus Vassa)
ca. 1745 – March 31, 1797

Kidnapped at the age of 11, shipped to America with his sister, from whom he was then separated, and sold into servitude, Olaudah Equiano began life as a slave "in a state of distraction not to be described. I cried and grieved continually; and for several days did not eat anything but what they forced into my mouth."

That he survived not only to escape slavery—Equiano purchased his freedom in 1766—but to write about it in what one critic has termed "the first truly notable book" in the genre of slave narrative, is testament both to Equiano's spirit and to his luck.

In his 1789 autobiography, *The Interesting Narrative of the Life of Olaudah Equiano, or Gustavus Vassa, the African, Written by Himself*, Equiano recounts the savage journey he was forced to make by ship to America and describes the violence he witnessed on arrival in Virginia, where slaves were branded like chattel and beaten for the least infraction of unwritten rules. He once saw a cook muzzled, her head bound in an iron contraption "which locked her mouth so fast that she could scarcely speak; and could not eat or drink."

Equiano was, relatively speaking, more fortunate. He eventually fell into the hands of a former officer of the Royal Navy, who took him to England and gave him preferential treatment (and a Latin name that Equiano resisted). En route to Britain, Equiano learned to read from a teenaged American sailor who befriended the African. "I had a great curiosity to talk to the books as I thought they did," Equiano recalled. "For that purpose I have often taken up a book and have talked to it and then put my ears to it, when in hopes it would answer me."

His peripatetic life took him into battle alongside his owner during the Seven Years War between France and Britain, and afterward back to America, where Equiano was sold to a new owner in Philadelphia, from whom he eventually bought his freedom. He later moved to England, learned the art of navigation, sailed the world, married, and fathered two daughters.

In Britain, Equiano became a formidable voice for the abolition movement, at one point petitioning the Queen to end slavery. When, at the age of 44, he embarked on a narrative of his life, Equiano did so in the hope that through his autobiography he might become "an instrument of my suffering countrymen." In this, he triumphed.

Nelson Algren
March 28, 1909 – May 9, 1981

In a sense, the two small boxing gloves tattooed on Nelson Algren's right arm said it all. Tough, combative, stubborn, Algren championed the underdogs of American life: the hobos, whores, inmates, and immigrants who filled cities like Algren's native Chicago in the middle years of the twentieth century. He said he did not know of a single writer who did not regard himself as a boxer.

Algren received his journalism degree from the University of Illinois in 1931, the heart of the Depression. He spent his first years out of college drifting among the jobless masses from Chicago to New Orleans and later the Southwest, the setting of his first published story, "So Help Me." Vanguard publishers noticed the story and offered Algren a small advance on a first novel. That work, *Somebody in Boots*, a picaresque account of an illiterate hobo's wanderings, appeared in 1935.

"It was dead-serious," Algren said later of the novel. "It was dead-serious because the author was dead-serious.... Survival was the story and revolution the theme." Disappointed by the book's lukewarm reception, Algren waited five years to publish his next book. In the meantime, he married and divorced the first of two wives.

His third novel, *The Man with the Golden Arm* (1949), the work for which Algren is best known, won the first National Book Award. Set in the slums of Chicago, the novel "shows up a rotted piece of U. S. life without indulging in a paragraph of preaching," said *Time* magazine. While at work on the book, Algren embarked on an on-again, off-again affair with Simone de Beauvoir, who toured America and parts of Latin America with Algren as her guide.

In the 1970s, Algren became obsessed with the story of Rubin "Hurricane" Carter, a former boxer jailed for murder on three consecutive life sentences. Algren believed, rightly, in Carter's innocence. The writer moved to New York to follow the case, and when *Esquire* turned down his article on Carter's second trial, Algren wrote a novel, *Calhoun*, based on the story. American publishers declined the book; it first appeared in 1981 in a German edition.

Having moved east, Algren vowed never to return, in life or death, to his "infamous city," Chicago. He died of heart failure at age 72 and is buried in a small whalers' graveyard in Sag Harbor, New York.

Sunday

24

Olive Schreiner, b. 1855   Palm Sunday

Monday

25

Toni Cade Bambara, b. 1939   *Mary Webb, b. 1881*   *Flannery O'Connor, b. 1925*

Tuesday

26

Christopher Marlowe, b. 1564
Joseph Campbell, b. 1904   *Robert Frost, b. 1874*   *Tennessee Williams, b. 1911*

Wednesday

27

Passover begins at sunset

Thursday

28

Nelson Algren, b. 1909   *Maxim Gorky, b. (Gregorian calendar) 1928*

Friday

29

Good Friday

Saturday

30

Sean O'Casey, b. 1880

March						
S	M	T	W	T	F	S
					1	2
3	4	5	6	7	8	9
10	11	12	13	14	15	16
17	18	19	20	21	22	23
24	25	26	27	28	29	30
31						

March
2002

April						
S	M	T	W	T	F	S
	1	2	3	4	5	6
7	8	9	10	11	12	13
14	15	16	17	18	19	20
21	22	23	24	25	26	27
28	29	30				

Sunday

31

Easter   *Andrew Marvell, b. 1621*   *Octavio Paz, b. 1914*

Monday

1

April Fools' Day
Easter Monday (Canada, U.K.)   *Matsuo Bashō, b. 1644*   *Edmond Rostand, b. 1868*

Tuesday

2

H.C. Andersen, b. 1805   Giacomo Girolamo Casanova, b. 1725   Flora Annie Steel, b. 1847

Wednesday

3

Washington Irving, b. 1783

Thursday

4

Marguerite Duras, b. 1914   Margaret Oliphant, b. 1828

Friday

5

Thomas Hobbes, b. 1588

Saturday

6

March						
S	M	T	W	T	F	S
					1	2
3	4	5	6	7	8	9
10	11	12	13	14	15	16
17	18	19	20	21	22	23
24	25	26	27	28	29	30
31						

March/April
2002

April						
S	M	T	W	T	F	S
	1	2	3	4	5	6
7	8	9	10	11	12	13
14	15	16	17	18	19	20
21	22	23	24	25	26	27
28	29	30				

Octavio Paz
March 31, 1914 – April 19, 1998

He so loved the garden outside his parents' home
on the outskirts of Mexico City that it became
"the center of my world." Likewise, the library
was "an enchanted cave" where a young Octavio
Paz read and played with his cousins and
schoolmates. "The world was limitless, yet it
was always within reach; time was a pliable
substance that weaved an unbroken present," he
said later of these halcyon years.

And then he woke up. A photograph in a
newspaper informed him one day of a recent war
(the First World War), and Paz abruptly realized
the existence of an outside world and his own
"unreality. I felt that the world was splitting, that
I did not inhabit the present."

He began to write poems, and soon realized it
was precisely his "expulsion from the present"
that prompted him to write—and would do so for the rest of Paz's 84 years. "Poetry is
in love with the instant, and seeks to relive it in the poem." "I was searching for the
gateway to the present; I wanted to belong to my time and to my century."

At 17, Paz published his first poem and founded the first of many literary reviews. By
age 20, he had issued his first book. He went on to write more than 40 books of poetry
and prose. In all of them, he reveals an abiding commitment to poetry. "Paz never lost
sight of poetry's irrational power and sacred mystery, its archaic roots, its spiritual
audacity," writes poet Edward Hirsch, a long-time Paz admirer.

Paz believed in a poet's civic responsibilities and at various junctures served as a
foreign diplomat for Mexico. He spent several years in India, a nation whose profound
influence on his life and work became the subject of his last book, *In Light of India*
(1995).

Convinced that the experience of being born constituted "a wound that never heals,"
Paz wrote poems that veer from isolation to connection, solitude to communion. He
viewed poetry and eroticism as fundamentally one activity, and argued that love, like
poetry, is a "victory over time."

Paz won the Nobel Prize for Literature in 1990. But he remained a humble man
devoted to his art and aware of its fragility. In the small poem "Escritura" ("Writing"),
he concedes, "I draw these letters / as the day draws its images / and blows over them
/ and does not return."

Donald Barthelme
April 7, 1931 – July 23, 1989

A book begins, he wrote, with a "slender intuition not much greater than an itch …The more serious the artist, the more problems he takes into account, the more considerations limit his possible initiatives."

Born in Philadelphia and raised in Houston, where his father was a professor of architecture at the

University of Houston, Barthelme recalled, "I was exposed to an almost religious crusade, the Modern movement in architecture. We were enveloped in Modernism. The house we lived in, which he'd designed, was Modern and the pictures were Modern and the books were Modern."

So, of course, Barthelme grew up to be a post-modernist, aligning himself with writers like John Barth, Thomas Pynchon, and William Gass, and particularly with the French poet Stéphane Mallarmé. Barthelme admired Mallarmé's ability to shake "words loose from their attachments and bestows new meanings upon them, meanings which point not toward the external world, but toward the Absolute, acts of poetic intuition."

Barthelme shook up the critical establishment with his own, innovative use of language. Hailed by some critics, he was blasted by others who deemed him a creator of havoc who celebrated unreason. Alfred Kazin complained that with Barthelme we have been "sentenced to the sentence." In fact, in one seven-page story, "Sentence," the entire story is one single sentence. In his first novel, *Snow White* (first published in *The New Yorker*), Barthelme used the language of politics, corporations, and advertising. His heroine longs for new words: "Oh I wish there were some words in the world that were not the words I always hear!"

Now collected into *Sixty Stories* (1981) and *Forty Stories* (1987), many of Barthelme's stories were first published in *The New Yorker,* and readers "had difficulty at first cottoning to writing like this," said his editor Roger Angell. "They were put off by Barthelme's crosscutting and by his terrifying absence of explanation, and those who resisted him in the end may have been people who were by nature unable to put their full trust in humor."

A friend once described him as a world-class worrier, and fear of the void is present in his work, but there's exultation as well as heartbreak. "How joyous the notion that, try as we may," Barthelme wrote, "we cannot do other than fail and fail absolutely, and that the task will remain always before us, like a meaning for our lives…"

Sunday

7

Gabriela Mistral, b. 1889   *Donald Barthelme, b. 1931*
William Wordsworth, b. 1770   Daylight Saving Time begins

Monday

8

Tuesday

9

Charles Baudelaire, b. 1821   Holocaust Remembrance Day

Wednesday

10

Clare Boothe Luce, b. 1903

Thursday

11

Friday

12

Saturday

13

Samuel Beckett, b. 1906   *Nella Larsen, b. 1891*

April						
S	M	T	W	T	F	S
	1	2	3	4	5	6
7	8	9	10	11	12	13
14	15	16	17	18	19	20
21	22	23	24	25	26	27
28	29	30				

April
2002

May						
S	M	T	W	T	F	S
			1	2	3	4
5	6	7	8	9	10	11
12	13	14	15	16	17	18
19	20	21	22	23	24	25
26	27	28	29	30	31	

Sunday
14

Monday
15

Henry James, b. 1843

Tuesday
16

Anatole France, b. 1844   J.M. Synge, b. 1871   Tristan Tzara, b. 1896

Wednesday
17

Henry Vaughan, b. 1622

Thursday
18

Isak Dinesen, b. 1885   Thornton Wilder, b. 1897

Friday
19

José Echegaray, b. 1832

Saturday
20

April						
S	M	T	W	T	F	S
	1	2	3	4	5	6
7	8	9	10	11	12	13
14	15	16	17	18	19	20
21	22	23	24	25	26	27
28	29	30				

April
2002

May						
S	M	T	W	T	F	S
			1	2	3	4
5	6	7	8	9	10	11
12	13	14	15	16	17	18
19	20	21	22	23	24	25
26	27	28	29	30	31	

Henry Vaughan
April 17, 1622 [?] – April 23, 1695

In his fifties, Henry Vaughan was asked if he wished to be included in a volume commemorating Oxford poets. Vaughan, who hadn't written anything in 20 years, was grateful. "I never was of such a magnitude as could invite you to take notice of me," he told his correspondent. Vaughan referred to himself as "low and forgotten."

His origins were equally unassuming. He was the oldest of twin boys born to Thomas and Denise Vaughan in the tiny community of Brecknockshire, Wales. He seems to have grown up in poverty. (The property Vaughan inherited at his father's death was valued at just five pounds.)

He briefly studied law and possibly medicine in Oxford and London. In London—"the Towne… of Drawers, Prentises, and boyes"—Vaughan availed himself of "rich Tobacco… / And royall, witty Sacke" in the city's innumerable taverns. But the outbreak of civil war sent him back to Wales in 1642, to the same piece of land where he'd grown up. Vaughan remained there for the rest of his life.

The outcome of the English Civil War, and specifically the Puritan suppression of the Anglican church, pushed Vaughan to give up the "idle verse" he'd been writing and commit his "poor Talent to the Church." The rich liturgical world of his childhood had vanished; in its place stood a "Wildernesse … a darksome, intricate wood full of Ambushes and dangers; a Forrest where spiritual hunters, principalities and powers spread their nets, and compasse it about."

For the next 15 years, Vaughan devoted himself to writing poetry and prose in which he sought to replicate and sustain the Anglican experience. In his two most famous works, *Silex Scintillans* ("The Glittering Flint"), a book-length poem published in two parts, and *The Mount of Olives*, a prose companion to the then-banned Book of Common Prayer, Vaughan laments what has been lost and encourages readers to trust in divine redemption.

He stopped writing at age 35. Although he lived another 40 years, no further event, political or personal, elicited a literary response from Henry Vaughan.

In later life, he practiced medicine, raised eight children (by two wives), and pursued life as a country gentleman in rural Wales. Vaughan's last years were consumed by legal actions taken by the children of one wife, who accused him of favoring the children of another. Vaughan did not resolve the suit until the final year of his life.

Ngaio Marsh
April 23, 1895 –
February 18, 1982

Her Maori name, pronounced "Nigh-o" has multiple meanings—"clever, light on the water, a little bug." It's an unlikely name for one of the grande dames of crime fiction. In fact, Marsh is often placed at the top of a group that includes Dorothy Sayers, Margery Allingham, and Agatha Christie.

Ngaio Marsh (r) with Agatha Christie

Perhaps it was the coincidence of sharing Shakespeare's birth date that turned her toward the theater and to mystery writing, or the influence of her English father and her New Zealand mother, both amateur actors and avid readers. Born and raised in Christchurch, New Zealand, Marsh was an only child, tall and gawky, with a deep voice. At 15, she studied art briefly, but after seeing a production of *Hamlet*, she fell in love with the theater. She produced plays for local theater groups and toured as an actor.

From 1928 to 1931, Marsh lived in England, supporting herself by running a gift shop and interior decorating. In 1931, on a rainy Sunday in London, she bought a few penny exercise books and some sharpened pencils. "I don't think that before or since this weekend I have ever written with less trouble and certainly never with less distinction," she said. Her first book, *A Man Lay Dead*, introduced her dashing detective Roderick Alleyn, named after the famous Elizabethan actor Edward Alleyn.

She divided her life between fiction and the theater and between New Zealand and England. In London, she hobnobbed with actors, prowled the Old Bailey, and strolled around Knightsbridge with her Siamese cat on a jeweled leash.

In over 30 best-selling novels, she wrote with charm, insight and humor. Her plots were surprising, and she devised ingenious murder weapons. In *Overture to Death*, a pistol in a piano is set to fire when the soft pedal is used in Rachmaninoff's "Prelude in C Sharp Minor." In *Light Thickens*, published after her death, the murders occur during performances of *Macbeth*. She described her style as "in the line of the original detective story, where a crime is solved calmly."

She never married, destroyed her correspondence, and refused to discuss her private life. Her autobiography was so unrevealing she joked that she should have called it "Other People." In 1966 she was made a Dame Commander of the British Empire, and in 1996 the Ngaio Marsh House Museum in Christchurch opened for visitors.

Sunday
21
Charlotte Brontë, b. 1816

Monday
22

Ellen Glasgow, b. 1873   Vladimir Nabokov, b. 1899   Madame de Staël, b. 1766

Tuesday
23

William Shakespeare, b. 1564   Bernard Malamud, b. 1914   Ngaio Marsh, b. 1895

Wednesday
24

Robert Penn Warren, b. 1905   William Goyen, b. 1915   Anthony Trollope, b. 1815

Thursday
25

Friday
26

Anita Loos, b. 1888   National Arbor Day

Saturday
27

Mary Wollstonecraft, b. 1759   Edward Gibbon, b. 1737

April						
S	M	T	W	T	F	S
	1	2	3	4	5	6
7	8	9	10	11	12	13
14	15	16	17	18	19	20
21	22	23	24	25	26	27
28	29	30				

April
2002

May						
S	M	T	W	T	F	S
			1	2	3	4
5	6	7	8	9	10	11
12	13	14	15	16	17	18
19	20	21	22	23	24	25
26	27	28	29	30	31	

Sunday
28

Monday
29

Tuesday
30

Wednesday
1

Joseph Heller, b. 1923

Thursday
2

Friday
3

May Sarton, b. 1912   Mikhail Bulgakov, b. 1891   William Inge, b. 1913   Niccolò Machiavelli, b. 1469

Saturday
4

T. H. Huxley, b. 1825

April						
S	M	T	W	T	F	S
	1	2	3	4	5	6
7	8	9	10	11	12	13
14	15	16	17	18	19	20
21	22	23	24	25	26	27
28	29	30				

April/May
2002

May						
S	M	T	W	T	F	S
			1	2	3	4
5	6	7	8	9	10	11
12	13	14	15	16	17	18
19	20	21	22	23	24	25
26	27	28	29	30	31	

Joseph Heller
May 1, 1923 – December 12, 1999

"You mean there's a catch?"

"Sure there's a catch," Doc Daneeka replied. "Catch-22. Anyone who wants to get out of combat duty isn't really crazy."

In the 1960s, thousands of college students who wanted to escape combat duty in the Vietnam War as well as soldiers who were fighting in Vietnam

identified with John Yossarian, the anti-hero survivor of Joseph Heller's first novel *Catch-22*. Although the novel was set during World War II, its black humor and devastating portrayal of an insane world spoke directly to a generation who thought their political and military leaders had gone mad. Poorly received by the critical establishment (*The New Yorker* critic wrote that it "gives the impression of having been shouted onto paper"), the book won a vast readership by word-of-mouth. Today, the novel has sold over ten million copies, and the term "Catch-22" has entered the language. The *Random House Unabridged Dictionary* defines it as "a frustrating situation in which one is trapped by contradictory regulations or conditions."

In *Catch-22,* Heller exaggerated and dramatized his own World War combat experiences as an Air Force bombadier flying 60 missions over Italy and France. He flew 37 missions before he felt afraid. After seeing his friends shot down, "I was scared even on the milk runs," he said. When he was discharged, he enrolled at the University of California and later earned a master's degree in literature from Columbia University. For years he earned a living in advertising and teaching, but he also published short stories. He received $25.00 for a story called "Catch-18." He expanded the story into a novel, but changed the title to *Catch-22* at the suggestion of his editor Robert Gottlieb.

Catch-22 reveals the dehumanizing, horrific effects of war, and it's hilarious. Even as a boy, Heller had possessed a skewed, comic view of the world. While growing up in Coney Island, he was addicted to amusement parks, practical jokes, and one-liners. "You've got a twisted brain," his mother often told him. He once wrote a school paper about the assassination of Abraham Lincoln from the viewpoint of the metal in the gun that was used to shoot him.

After the spectacular success of *Catch-22*, Heller published other novels, including *Something Happened, Good as Gold*, and *God Knows*. But his first novel was his masterpiece, and he knew it. Once, during an interview, Heller was told that he had never written anything better than *Catch-22*. "Who has?" he replied.

Gregorio Martínez Sierra
May 6, 1881 – October 1, 1947

As a ten-year-old, Gregorio Martínez Sierra produced and directed his own version of *Robinson Crusoe* for his neighborhood friends. By then he was already writing dialogues, an activity he continued when, at 14, he founded an amateur acting troupe, *El Porvenir* ("The Future"). He aimed for his own future to be theatrical, too.

At the University of Madrid, Martínez Sierra was an indifferent student who soon dropped out, bored with the formalities of the classroom. Sickly and despondent, he coughed dreadfully and convinced himself he was "destined to die young and sad."

But he survived to fall in love with a fellow student, María de la O Lejárraga, who began collaborating with him on his literary pursuits. By the time they married in 1900 (Gregorio was 19, María 25), they had published five collections of poems, plays, and stories. Although jointly composed, the works appeared under Gregorio's name alone; decades passed before the public knew the full scope of María's contribution. Ironically, critics regarded his insight into female characters as the single most distinguishing feature of Martínez Sierra's plays. His most famous collaboration with María was *Canción de cuna*, or "Cradle Song." (Paramount Pictures made a film of it in 1933.)

In 1916, Martínez Sierra founded the Teatro Eslava in Madrid. He shaped the company's repertoire of classical and contemporary works with the aim of combating the trite bourgeois theatre then prevalent in the capital. He was especially fond of Maurice Maeterlinck's symbolist drama. He staged works by Manuel de Falla and premiered Federico García Lorca's first play. A fervent patron of the arts, he also established and ran several literary journals.

Sometime after founding the Eslava, Martínez Sierra began a lifelong affair with the company's leading actress, Catalina Bárcena.

A small man with a domed brow and black eyes who dressed impeccably, Martínez Sierra had tastes to match the exquisite nature of his personality. He collected antique jewels, porcelain, and fine glassware. He loved nature. A frustrated composer, he liked to listen to music in bed in the mornings while he read. His poetic and theatrical instincts were lyrical.

"Words are constant friends, discreet companions of our solitude," he once remarked. "… I enjoy beautiful words as much as I enjoy looking at flowers." Words, he added, are "as indefinite as hope. In them, meaning is transitory."

Sunday

5

Monday

6

Sigmund Freud, b. 1856   Gregorio Martínez Sierra, b. 1881   May Day Holiday (U.K.)

Tuesday

7

Archibald MacLeish, b. 1892   Rabindranath Tagore, b. 1861   Edward Lear, b. 1812

Wednesday

8

Edmund Wilson, b. 1895

Thursday

9

James M. Barrie, b. 1860

Friday

10

Benito Pérez Galdós, b. 1843

Saturday

11

Mari Sandoz, b. 1896

May						
S	M	T	W	T	F	S
				1	2	3	4
5	6	7	8	9	10	11
12	13	14	15	16	17	18
19	20	21	22	23	24	25
26	27	28	29	30	31	

May
2002

June						
S	M	T	W	T	F	S
						1
2	3	4	5	6	7	8
9	10	11	12	13	14	15
16	17	18	19	20	21	22
23	24	25	26	27	28	29
30						

Sunday
12

Mother's Day   *Daphne du Maurier, b. 1907*

Monday
13

Tuesday
14

Dante Alighieri, b. 1265

Wednesday
15

L. Frank Baum, b. 1856
Clifton Fadiman, b. 1904   *Katherine Anne Porter, b. 1890*   *Arthur Schnitzler, b. 1862*

Thursday
16

Shavuot begins at sunset

Friday
17

Dorothy Richardson, b. 1873

Saturday
18

Armed Forces Day   *Bertrand Russell, b. 1872*

May						
S	M	T	W	T	F	S
			1	2	3	4
5	6	7	8	9	10	11
12	13	14	15	16	17	18
19	20	21	22	23	24	25
26	27	28	29	30	31	

May
2002

June						
S	M	T	W	T	F	S
						1
2	3	4	5	6	7	8
9	10	11	12	13	14	15
16	17	18	19	20	21	22
23	24	25	26	27	28	29
30						

Clifton Fadiman
May 15, 1904 – June 20, 1999

In a sense, his career began at age four, when Clifton Fadiman learned to read. He never stopped. Even in his late eighties, almost blind, he listened to unabridged books on tape so that he could continue to vet manuscripts for the Book-of-the-Month Club (which he helped found), as he had since 1944. "One's first book, kiss, or home run is always the best," Fadiman said. Who knew better than he?

Blessed with a genuinely encyclopedic memory, he could read 80 pages an hour. To create his 700-page *Treasury of the Encyclopedia Britannica*, Fadiman read or skimmed some 200 years' worth of editions of the reference. In his seventies, he learned to read child-level Italian, Spanish, Swedish, and Dutch in order to write a Britannica entry on the history of children's literature.

"I am not a profound thinker," he said. Rather, Fadiman viewed himself as a guide who could help other readers pick the titles most appropriate for them. In the introduction to his *Lifetime Reading Plan*, which he revised (with John S. Major) in his nineties, Fadiman argued that great books are "life companions. Once part of you, they work in and on and with you until you die. They should not be read in a hurry, any more than friends are made in a hurry."

He urged young readers to embrace classic literature: "Books are not rolls, to be devoured only when they are fresh."

The Brooklyn-born son of Russian-Jewish immigrants, Kip (his childhood nickname) Fadiman married twice; had three children; became a top editor at Simon & Schuster and a book reviewer for the *New Yorker*; appeared on a variety of radio shows, most notably "Quiz Kids"; and published more than two dozen anthologies, plus a compendium on wine.

Of his lifelong devotion to wine, Fadiman revealed, "I think of ourselves as a model couple—faithful, mutually solicitous, still ardent, and in the case of the lady, well preserved."

He understood that "we all die uneducated." But by reading the world's great books, he said, "at least we will not feel quite so lost, so bewildered. We will have disenthralled ourselves from the merely contemporary."

Fadiman had a penchant for people's last words, and once wrote an essay called "Some Passing Remarks on Some Passing Remarks." His favorite parting line, he confessed, was that of the 18th-century British writer Mary Wortley Montague: "It has all been very interesting."

Where Language Ceases
[May 19 – May 25, 2002]

It's all too easy to ridicule opera. A hero, mortally wounded, succumbs to his injuries only *after* he performs a majestic aria. A heroine, near death from consumption, emits a wisp of a cough and launches into a soaring melody. "A dying man is real," said Bertolt Brecht. "If he sings at the same time, we have reached the sphere of absurdity."

His mockery of the form notwithstanding, Brecht collaborated with Kurt Weill on two operatic works, *The Threepenny Opera* and *The Rise and Fall of the City of Mahagonny*. The latter, Brecht claimed, "pays conscious tribute to the absurdity of the operatic form."

Moved to reflect on opera, any number of writers have proved ambivalent. The Austrian poet and essayist Hugo von Hofmannsthal voiced his discomfort at "how short is the libretto of *Tristan* and how long the opera." After witnessing his first French opera, John Dryden decried the "French machines [that] have never done England good." (Dryden couldn't resist subsequently trying his hand at a libretto, however.) Voltaire described the Paris Opéra as a "public gathering place where one meets on certain days without quite knowing why."

Born in Florence, in the age of Lope de Vega and Shakespeare, opera sprang from a misbegotten attempt to re-create the sung drama of ancient Greece. By 1607, when Monteverdi premiered *Orfeo*, opera had evolved into a predominantly musical, not literary, genre, and had begun to earn the scorn of the literary world. Eventually, the two worlds reconciled in the figure of the librettist, who weds play to music to create a truly lyric theater.

For countless writers opera is an infinite source of inspiration. The playwright Terrence McNally is a regular on the Metropolitan Opera's Saturday afternoon opera quiz. George Bernard Shaw fell irretrievably in love with music when, as a boy, he heard his mother sing a passage from Meyerbeer's *Les Huguenots*. W. H. Auden wrote that "its pure artifice renders opera the ideal dramatic medium for a tragic myth."

After hearing the quartet in *Rigoletto*, Victor Hugo exclaimed, "Ah, if I only could in my play make four people talk simultaneously in a way that the public would understand the words and the varying sentiments."

Tragic, grandiose, seductive, and ultimately impenetrable, opera remains, in the words of music critic Paul Henry Lang, both "a magnificent compromise" and "an eternal lesson of the power and scope of music." As Kierkegaard advised, "Where language ceases, music begins."

Sunday
19

Malcolm X, b. 1925   Lorraine Hansberry, b. 1930

Monday
20

Margery Allingham, b. 1904   Honoré de Balzac, b. 1799   Victoria Day (Canada)

Tuesday
21

Alexander Pope, b. 1688

Wednesday
22

Sir Arthur Conan Doyle, b. 1859

Thursday
23

Friday
24

Joseph Brodsky, b. 1940   Mawlid, Prophet Mohammed born c. 570

Saturday
25

Ralph Waldo Emerson, b. 1803   Raymond Carver, b. 1938   Theodore Roethke, b. 1908

			May			
S	M	T	W	T	F	S
			1	2	3	4
5	6	7	8	9	10	11
12	13	14	15	16	17	18
19	20	21	22	23	24	25
26	27	28	29	30	31	

May
2002

			June			
S	M	T	W	T	F	S
						1
2	3	4	5	6	7	8
9	10	11	12	13	14	15
16	17	18	19	20	21	22
23	24	25	26	27	28	29
30						

Sunday

26

Isadora Duncan, b. 1877

Monday

27

Memorial Day
Spring Holiday (U.K.)   *Rachel Carson, b. 1907   Dashiell Hammett, b. 1894   John Cheever, b. 1912*

Tuesday

28

Patrick White, b. 1912

Wednesday

29

Thursday

30

Countee Cullen, b. 1903

Friday

31

Walt Whitman, b. 1819

Saturday

1

May						
S	M	T	W	T	F	S
			1	2	3	4
5	6	7	8	9	10	11
12	13	14	15	16	17	18
19	20	21	22	23	24	25
26	27	28	29	30	31	

May/June
2002

June						
S	M	T	W	T	F	S
						1
2	3	4	5	6	7	8
9	10	11	12	13	14	15
16	17	18	19	20	21	22
23	24	25	26	27	28	29
30						

Isadora Duncan
May 26, 1877 – September 14, 1927

In her autobiography, written in the last years of her life and published posthumously, Isadora Duncan portrayed herself as a tempestuous bohemian flitting from one love affair to the next, dancing and dazzling audiences in between. She carefully hid the dark side of her existence. "No woman has ever told the truth about her life," she declared.

Born in San Francisco in 1877, the granddaughter of Irish immigrants who pushed their way west across America in a covered wagon, Duncan grew up in near-poverty. Her parents divorced before she was one. Left alone while their mother worked, Isadora and her three siblings climbed trees, staged theatricals, and led generally unsupervised lives.

She learned to dance from her older sister, and was soon laboring to create the maverick, uniquely American style for which she later became famous: an uncorseted body, bare legs and feet, gesture stripped of titillation, movement as the embodiment of thought. When Duncan went to Paris in her early twenties to launch her career, she galvanized audiences, and the legendary "Isadora" was born.

She toured Europe as a soloist for the next two decades, had two children by two different men, and rarely lost a chance to shock contemporaries with her lavish lifestyle, rash outbursts, and string of lovers.

In 1913, Duncan's children both drowned in a freak car accident, and a desolate Isadora plunged into depression and alcoholism. She struggled to keep dancing.

Words provided some solace. She had loved books and libraries as a child. As an adult, she read widely; philosophers such as Darwin and Nietszche were fundamental to Duncan's understanding of both art and life. "We must have Philosophy," she said. "Without that we would die of pain like dumb brutes."

She wrote throughout her life: treatises on the dance, manifestos (both political and artistic), letters. In the last year of her life, impelled in part by the urging of admirers and in larger part by the need for money, Duncan undertook her memoirs. Published shortly after her death, *My Life* remains in print today and is a vital inspiration to countless young artists.

Duncan professed to have known but two motives in her life, love and art. "Often Love destroyed Art, and often the imperious call of Art put a tragic end to Love," she wrote. "For these two have no accord but only constant battle."

Marquis de Sade
June 2, 1740 – December 2, 1814

"Must we burn de Sade?" asked Simone de Beauvoir in an essay. Her answer was a measured no. During a life spent mostly in prison and in an insane asylum, de Sade wrote some 100 works. Many were lost, and his most famous books, *Justine, The Bedroom Philosophers*, and *The 120 Days of Sodom* are rarely read today.

He was born Donatien Alphonse Francoix, Marquis de Sade, and his name gave us the word "sadism." At four, he was removed from his mother and cared for by his depraved uncle, a clergyman. He entered a Jesuit College in Paris, became a cavalry officer, and married the daughter of a prominent family. Six months after his wedding, he was sent to jail for violence against prostitutes. After his release, he could not give up his debauched life, and in February 1777 he was again arrested and sent to the dungeon of Vincennes. Seven years later he was moved to the Bastille in Paris.

"Yes, I admit I am a libertine," de Sade protested, "and in that area I have imagined everything that can be imagined … I am a libertine, but I am not a criminal or a murderer."

He was, though, despite his shocking subject matter, a pedestrian and amateurish writer. In the Bastille, he wrote *The 120 Days of Sodom,* which contains graphic descriptions of sexual perversions. He was transferred to the insane asylum at Charenton, where he wrote his novel *Justine*. In the novel, de Sade contrasts the lives of two sisters, the virtuous Justine and the wicked Juliet. "The design of this novel is undoubtedly unique," de Sade wrote. "Here vice is shown everywhere triumphant, and virtue the victim of its own sacrifices." As an illustration of this thesis, Justine (and her virtue) are destroyed at the end of the novel by a "blinding bolt of lightning."

His influence as a thinker is out of proportion with his ability as a writer. Yet, argues, Camille Paglia, de Sade must be read and "confronted in all his ugliness."

"Mad indeed is he who adopts a way of thinking for others!" de Sade wrote. "My way of thinking is the fruit of my reflections… I am not free to change…it lightens all my woes in prison, it composes all my pleasures in the world and I care more for it than for life." He died in Charenton.

Sunday
2

Thomas Hardy, b. 1840   Barbara Pym, b. 1913   Marquis de Sade, b. 1740   Dorothy West, b. 1907

Monday
3

Allen Ginsberg, b. 1926

Tuesday
4

Wednesday
5

Federico García Lorca, b. 1898

Thursday
6

Thomas Mann, b. 1875

Friday
7

Elizabeth Bowen, b. 1889

Saturday
8

Marguerite Yourcenar, b. 1903

June						
S	M	T	W	T	F	S
						1
2	3	4	5	6	7	8
9	10	11	12	13	14	15
16	17	18	19	20	21	22
23	24	25	26	27	28	29
30						

June
2002

July						
S	M	T	W	T	F	S
	1	2	3	4	5	6
7	8	9	10	11	12	13
14	15	16	17	18	19	20
21	22	23	24	25	26	27
28	29	30	31			

Sunday

9

Monday

10

Tuesday

11

Ben Jonson, b. 1572

Wednesday

12

Djuna Barnes, b. 1892   Anne Frank, b. 1929   Harriet Martineau, b. 1802   Dorothy L. Sayers, b. 1893

Thursday

13

Fanny Burney, b. 1752   William Butler Yeats, b. 1865

Friday

14

Flag Day   Jerzy Kosinski, b. 1933   Harriet Beecher Stowe, b. 1811

Saturday

15

June						
S	M	T	W	T	F	S
						1
2	3	4	5	6	7	8
9	10	11	12	13	14	15
16	17	18	19	20	21	22
23	24	25	26	27	28	29
30						

June
2002

July						
S	M	T	W	T	F	S
	1	2	3	4	5	6
7	8	9	10	11	12	13
14	15	16	17	18	19	20
21	22	23	24	25	26	27
28	29	30	31			

Harriet Martineau
June 12, 1802 – June 27, 1876

"I am, in truth, very thankful for not having married at all," said Harriet Martineau. In truth, how could she have found the time?

One of the most prominent intellectuals of her age, Martineau was an essayist, novelist, historian, economics and travel writer, and an autobiographer who wrote a staggering number of books. Her first best-seller, *Illustrations of Political Economy* (1832–34), ran to 25 volumes, and was a series of tales, each one illustrating an economic principle.

She spent two years traveling in America and collected her impressions into a three-volume work titled *Society in America* (1837). After studying female education in the United States, she believed that its primary purpose was to train women "to consider marriage as the sole object in life, and to pretend that they do not think so." Her realistic opinions on marriage were remarkable not because she believed them, but because she felt free to publish them. "Any one must see at a glance that if men and women marry those whom they do not love, they must love those whom they do not marry," she wrote.

The sixth child in a family of eight, Martineau grew up in Norwich, England. Educated at home, she read Milton's *Paradise Lost* at seven, was a "walking concordance of Shakespeare," and claimed to "think in Latin." Intellectually precocious, she was physically frail. She was also plain and obstinate, with no sense of taste or smell. She became deaf during adolescence and used an ear trumpet for the rest of her life. When her father died in 1826, and she was forced to support herself, she took in needlework and began writing. She said she liked being poor because it offered her "a scope for action."

In 1839, the same year her best novel *Deerbrook* was published, she fell ill. Five years later, she claimed to have been completely cured by mesmerism. Everything was fodder for her relentless pen, and she wrote up her illness in *Life in the Sickroom: or Essays by an Invalid* (1844). In 1845 she built a home called "The Knoll" in the Lake District. Charlotte Brontë, George Eliot, and the Wordsworths all visited her there. Brontë characterized Martineau as "both hard and warm-hearted, abrupt and affectionate."

After her death, *The Times* declared, "If any lady of the 19th century…may be allowed to put in a claim for the credit of not having lived in vain, that woman, we honestly believe, was Harriet Martineau."

H. Rider Haggard
June 22, 1856 – May 14, 1925

A childhood nursemaid discovered the perfect way to keep young Rider Haggard quiet at night. After settling the boy in bed, the nurse would open a bedroom cupboard to reveal an ugly doll with black wool hair and a sinister leer. This was "She-who-must-be-obeyed," the nurse informed her charge, and then left Haggard to fend for himself in the dark.

A self-described romantic, Haggard seized on this and other boyhood memories to explain the prolific imagination he later harnessed to write more than 50 novels, short-story collections, essays, and autobiography. Peopled by African queens, ancient demigoddesses, magicians, witch doctors, Zulu warriors, and 10th-century kings, and set in locales as exotic (to 19th-century eyes) as Egypt and Rhodesia, Haggard's fiction blends mystery, fantasy, and romance to forge the quintessential adventure story.

He was a sickly infant who grew into a dreamy adolescent. His dictatorial father forced the teenaged Haggard to give up the girl he loved in exchange for a career with the British Foreign Office. At 19, Haggard was dispatched to South Africa, where he remained for the better part of six years. It was the start of a life of travel that would carry him throughout the world and inspire book after book.

He wrote one of his first, and to this day best-known, books, *King Solomon's Mines*, in six weeks on a dare from one of his brothers. *King Solomon's* came out in 1885 and sold 31,000 copies in one year. A second, equally acclaimed novel, *She*, followed. Haggard's long and uneven reign as one of Britain's most popular 19th-century writers began.

After reading an early Haggard draft, a colleague counseled him, "You have written it with your *left hand* without strenuous pains; you must rewrite it with your *right hand*, throwing all your force into it." While Haggard initially heeded this advice, he failed to follow through. His later novels, most of them written after the devastating loss of Haggard's mother and his only son in the early 1890s, are uninspired imitations of early successes. Haggard worked by rote, chiefly to pay the bills.

He left his mark nonetheless. Robert Louis Stevenson and Rudyard Kipling both admired him; Sigmund Freud recommended his books to a patient. But Haggard's greatest legacy is cinematic. As long as lost cities, Egyptian curses, and heroes such as Indiana Jones populate our movies, H. Rider Haggard is with us.

Sunday
16
Father's Day

 Monday
17

James Weldon Johnson, b. 1871   *John Hersey, b. 1914*

Tuesday
18

Philip Barry, b. 1896

Wednesday
19

Blaise Pascal, b. 1623

Thursday
20

Lillian Hellman, b. 1905

Friday
21

Mary McCarthy, b. 1912   Summer Solstice, 9:24 am EDT

Saturday
22

H. Rider Haggard, b. 1856   *Erich Maria Remarque, b. 1898*

		June				
S	**M**	**T**	**W**	**T**	**F**	**S**
						1
2	3	4	5	6	7	8
9	10	11	12	13	14	15
16	17	18	19	20	21	22
23	24	25	26	27	28	29
30						

June
2002

		July				
S	**M**	**T**	**W**	**T**	**F**	**S**
	1	2	3	4	5	6
7	8	9	10	11	12	13
14	15	16	17	18	19	20
21	22	23	24	25	26	27
28	29	30	31			

Sunday
23
Anna Akhmatova, b. 1889   Jean Anouilh, b. 1910

Monday
24

Ambrose Bierce, b. 1842   St. John of the Cross, b. 1542

Tuesday
25

George Orwell, b. 1903

Wednesday
26

Pearl Buck, b. 1892

Thursday
27

Paul Laurence Dunbar, b. 1872   Helen Keller, b. 1880

Friday
28

Luigi Pirandello, b. 1867   Esther Forbes, b. 1891

Saturday
29
Antoine de Saint-Exupéry, b. 1900

June						
S	M	T	W	T	F	S
						1
2	3	4	5	6	7	8
9	10	11	12	13	14	15
16	17	18	19	20	21	22
23	24	25	26	27	28	29
30						

June
2002

July						
S	M	T	W	T	F	S
	1	2	3	4	5	6
7	8	9	10	11	12	13
14	15	16	17	18	19	20
21	22	23	24	25	26	27
28	29	30	31			

Jean Anouilh
June 23, 1910 – October 3, 1987

One critic punned that his name was just a variant spelling of "ennui." Another sniped that he just wrote "Big Roles for Big Actors." Richard Burton, Ralph Richardson, Julie Harris, Eve Le Gallienne, and Laurence Olivier all starred in Anouilh plays. His work was also popular with audiences in France, England, and on Broadway—a fact that irritated Edmund Wilson. "One of the chief problems of modern life," Wilson declared, "is to avoid seeing Anouilh's plays." Anouilh's best scripts, *The Rehearsal, Antigone, The Lark, Waltz of the Toreadors, Becket,* and *Ring Round the Moon,* still continue to be produced today despite the difficulties of translation. "Turning certain plays from French into English is like dragging vampires into the sunlight," Ben Brantley wrote in the *New York Times.* "They shriek, they curdle, they shrivel, while shedding the elegant, arrogant authority they display in their natural element."

Born and raised near Bordeaux in southwest France, the son of a poor tailor, Anouilh was a solitary boy without close friends. He began writing plays as a teenager, studied law for a time, and worked briefly as an advertising copywriter, which he found a good preparation for playwriting. "A slogan," he said, "presupposes a precision of words within a phrase that resembles the strictness necessary for lines in a play."

In the early 1930s, Anouilh struggled as a working playwright. He and his actress wife furnished their apartment with stage furniture, and their daughter's crib was a bureau drawer from the set of *Siegfried.* When he sold Hollywood the film rights to a play, he bought a house, but he always disparaged movies. "I write plays because that is all I know how to do," he said, "and I write them the way my father used to cut his suits." Noted for his technical versatility and precise language coupled with dazzling theatricality, Anouilh grouped his plays into types—black plays, jarring plays, pink plays, glittering plays, and costume plays. Anouilh felt that theatre should "create by every artifice possible something truer than truth."

Sometimes Anouilh's truth was ambiguous. During World War II, his version of *Antigone* was claimed by the French Resistance and by the collaborators—the Resistance praised the character of Antigone and the collaborators sided with Creon. At the end of the play, however, the chorus presented another, more cynical view, "Only the guards are left, and none of this matters to them. It's no skin off their noses. They go on playing cards."

Isaac Babel
July 1 (July 13), 1894 – March 17, 1941

In his tenth year, the Russian-born Isaac Babel became fully aware of what it meant to be a Jew. The disdain his teachers showed for Jewish schoolboys, the discrimination against Jews who wished to pursue a higher education, the pogroms to which he was an uncomprehending witness—all combined to afflict Babel with a nervous condition that plagued him for life.

In the first of his known works, the story "Old Shloyme," Babel tells of a Jewish family forced either to renounce their faith or leave their home. The key figure in the story is an 86-year-old Jewish man whose mind is deteriorating.

With the encouragement of Maxim Gorky, whom he met when he was 22, Babel published further stories in prestigious journals. His fiction is distinguished by its clarity and concision. Some stories contain no sentence longer than three lines. "Perhaps the sentences I write are too short," Babel acknowledged. "Partly because of my everlasting asthma. I can't speak for any length of time."

His pronouncements on style are matchless. "A phrase is born into the world good and bad at the same time," he declared. "The secret lies in a twist barely perceptible. The lever must lie in the hand and grow warm there. It must be turned once, but not twice." And: "Only a genius can permit himself two adjectives with a single noun."

His most celebrated collection, *Red Cavalry*, inspired by his experiences as a soldier in the Russian army, consists of 35 stories, the longest just seven pages, the shortest under a page. The collection is narrated by a bespectacled Jewish unbeliever, not unlike Babel himself.

His life was in some ways as elliptical as his art. He fathered a daughter by his wife and a second daughter by his lover. His wife, daughter, and various relatives fled Russia to settle in Paris, but although he deigned to visit them, Babel could not bring himself to stay. "Spiritual life is nobler in Russia. I am poisoned by Russia, I long for it, I think only of Russia," he said.

He paid the highest price for his loyalty. Accused of nothing in particular, but like so many of his compatriots, suspected of all, he was arrested in 1939. A certificate—issued in 1954—indicates that Babel died of unspecified causes on March 17, 1941. Many of his later works, including two unfinished novels, vanished. Only his remarkable stories remain.

Sunday

30

Monday

1

Isaac Babel, b. 1894   George Sand, b. 1804   Susan Glaspell, b. 1873   Canada Day

---

 Tuesday

2

Charlotte Perkins Gilman, b. 1860   Franz Kafka, b. 1883

Wednesday

3

M.F.K. Fisher, b. 1908

Thursday

4

Nathaniel Hawthorne, b. 1804   Declaration of Independence, 1776

Friday

5

Jean Cocteau, b. 1889

Saturday

6

June						
S	M	T	W	T	F	S
						1
2	3	4	5	6	7	8
9	10	11	12	13	14	15
16	17	18	19	20	21	22
23	24	25	26	27	28	29
30						

June/July
2002

July						
S	M	T	W	T	F	S
	1	2	3	4	5	6
7	8	9	10	11	12	13
14	15	16	17	18	19	20
21	22	23	24	25	26	27
28	29	30	31			

Sunday

7

Robert A. Heinlein, b. 1907

Monday

8

Tuesday

9

Wednesday

10

Marcel Proust, b. 1871

Thursday

11

E.B. White, b. 1899

Friday

12

Bruno Schulz, b. 1892
Madame Blavatsky, b. 1831   Pablo Neruda, b. 1904   Henry D. Thoreau, b. 1817   Johanna Spyri, b. 1827

Saturday

13

July						
S	M	T	W	T	F	S
	1	2	3	4	5	6
7	8	9	10	11	12	13
14	15	16	17	18	19	20
21	22	23	24	25	26	27
28	29	30	31			

July
2002

August						
S	M	T	W	T	F	S
				1	2	3
4	5	6	7	8	9	10
11	12	13	14	15	16	17
18	19	20	21	22	23	24
25	26	27	28	29	30	31

The Gothic Novel

Battlements of haunted castles, gloomy monasteries, ancient ruins, wild landscapes lit by lighting, hollow voices echoing in shadowy courts, brutal villains, terrified, helpless young women—all these and more are present in the gothic novel. The form, says scholar Maggie Kilgour, is a "Frankenstein's monster, assembled out of the bits and pieces of the past."

The gothic novel first took root in the late18th century when the impending French Revolution threatened English peace. Horace Walpole, the son of the English Prime Minister, initiated the genre with *The Castle of Otranto* (1765). Fascinated with everything medieval, he even transformed his country estate into a fake Gothic castle. Walpole confessed that the book had come to him in a dream. "I had thought myself in an ancient castle… and that on the upper-most banister of a great staircase I saw a gigantic hand in armour." He began to write, not knowing where his story would lead. He completed the book in less than two months.

In 1794, Ann Radcliffe placed a woman at the center of her novel *The Mysteries of Udolpho* and began a craze for the Gothic that continues today. The wife of a London newspaper editor, Radcliffe "never appeared in public, nor mingled in private society, but kept herself apart, like the sweet bird that sings its solitary notes, shrouded and unseen." Because of her elusive character and because secrecy and suspense pervaded her novels, rumors circulated that she was insane.

Jane Austen's characters in *Northanger Abbey* read *Udolpho* and other "horrid" novels of the day. Austen's parody of the gothic novel is knowing and delicious. Alone in her room on a stormy night in Northanger Abbey, Catherine explores an old chest. Just as she is about to examine a mysterious manuscript she finds hidden in the chest, a violent gust of wind blows out her candle. She spends a disturbing night, the storm rages, "hollow murmurs creep along the gallery, and more than once her blood was chilled by the sound of distant moans." In the bright morning, though, when she examines the manuscript, she discovers that it's nothing more than an inventory of laundry. "Nothing could now be clearer than the absurdity of her recent fancies," writes Austen.

Yet, argued Ann Radcliffe, "what ardent imagination ever was contented to trust to plain reasoning, or to the evidence of the senses?"

THE

MYSTERIES OF UDOLPHO,

A

R O M A N C E;

INTERSPERSED WITH SOME PIECES OF POETRY.

BY

ANN RADCLIFFE,

AUTHOR OF THE ROMANCE OF THE FOREST, ETC.

IN FOUR VOLUMES.

Fate fits on thefe dark battlements, and frowns,
And, as the portals open to receive me,
Her voice, in fullen echoes through the courts,
Tells of a namelefs deed.

VOL. I.

LONDON:
PRINTED FOR G. G. AND J. ROBINSON,
PATERNOSTER-ROW.
1794.

Iris Murdoch
July 15, 1919 – February 8, 1999

"Writers of brief and meticulous articles will always look askance at writers of large, unrigorous, emotional volumes," Iris Murdoch remarked in 1957, after publishing her first two novels. "But the latter, for better or worse, have the last word."

She was her own best example. Married to Oxford don John Bayley, Murdoch herself taught philosophy at Oxford for 15 years before turning full-time to writing. In a four-decade career, she produced 26 novels, a half-dozen works on philosophy, several plays, poems, and critical essays on literature, modern ideas, and poetry. On average, she published a novel every two years, sometimes pausing just 30 minutes between the end of one novel and the start of the next.

She shunned word processors and typewriters. She planned each of her novels in its entirety before setting pen to paper. She wrote first drafts in longhand, leaving wide margins for notes, and then revised. She refused to let her publishers make changes or edits—a practice that occasioned complaints from critics who thought Murdoch's longer works needed pruning.

An only child, she grew up in what she later described as "a perfect trinity of love." Her mother, a former opera singer, instilled in Murdoch a happy temperament and a lifelong fondness for music. Her father, who loved books, encouraged her to read widely. In her own long marriage to Bayley, Murdoch re-created the quiet, secure, intellectually and artistically stimulating life she had known with her parents.

She rarely read modern writers. She favored 19th-century British and European novelists, "moralistic writers," she said, "who portray the complexity of morality and the difficulty of being good." Her own books—among them the award-winning *The Sea, the Sea*; *The Black Prince*; and *The Sacred and Profane Love Machine*—reveal Murdoch's enduring preoccupation with love and art, and with the possibility and difficulty of doing good and avoiding evil. A.S. Byatt has argued that all of Murdoch's novels are to an extent "studies of the 'degrees of freedom' available to individuals."

In 1995, Murdoch complained in an interview that she was experiencing writer's block. In 1996, John Bayley announced that his wife had Alzheimer's. He wrote movingly of that grim diagnosis and his last years with Murdoch in *Elegy for Iris*.

Iris Murdoch died on February 8, 1999, with Bayley at her bedside. A few years earlier, she had confessed to a friend that she was "sailing into the darkness."

Sunday

14

Natalia Ginzburg, b. 1916   *F.R. Leavis, b. 1895*   *Isaac Bashevis Singer, b. 1904*   *Irving Stone, b. 1903*

Monday

15

Iris Murdoch, b. 1919

Tuesday

16

Caroline Blackwood, b. 1931

 Wednesday

17

Thursday

18

William Makepeace Thackeray, b. 1811

Friday

19

Saturday

20

Petrarch, b. 1304

July						
S	M	T	W	T	F	S
	1	2	3	4	5	6
7	8	9	10	11	12	13
14	15	16	17	18	19	20
21	22	23	24	25	26	27
28	29	30	31			

July
2002

August						
S	M	T	W	T	F	S
				1	2	3
4	5	6	7	8	9	10
11	12	13	14	15	16	17
18	19	20	21	22	23	24
25	26	27	28	29	30	31

Sunday
21
Hart Crane, b. 1899   John Gardner, b. 1933   Ernest Hemingway, b. 1899   Diana Trilling, b. 1905

Monday
22

Emma Lazarus, b. 1849

Tuesday
23

Raymond Chandler, b. 1888

Wednesday
24

Alexandre Dumas, père, b. 1802

Thursday
25

Friday
26

Carl Jung, b. 1875   George Bernard Shaw, b. 1856   Antonio Machado, b. 1875

Saturday
27
Alexandre Dumas, fils, b. 1824

July						
S	M	T	W	T	F	S
	1	2	3	4	5	6
7	8	9	10	11	12	13
14	15	16	17	18	19	20
21	22	23	24	25	26	27
28	29	30	31			

July
2002

August						
S	M	T	W	T	F	S
				1	2	3
4	5	6	7	8	9	10
11	12	13	14	15	16	17
18	19	20	21	22	23	24
25	26	27	28	29	30	31

Raymond Chandler
July 23, 1888 – March 26, 1959

At 68, two years before his death, Raymond Chandler felt that he had lived his entire life "on the edge of nothing."

Writing edgy, hard-boiled detective fiction about a "world gone wrong," Chandler transformed the genre's conventions of brutality, sex, and blood into artful literature. "His prose is without ornament," said Robert Parker. "It is as functional as a Shaker table."

Lowbrows and highbrows read Chandler. During the 1940s Evelyn Waugh called him "the greatest living American novelist." Oddly, Chandler's most profound influence was the classical education he received at Dulwich College in England. Born in Chicago and raised in Nebraska, Chandler moved to Ireland with his family when he was seven. Later, he spent four years in London writing essays, poetry, and book reviews. He described himself as "an elegant young thing trying to be brilliant about nothing."

In 1912, he returned to the United States and worked in a series of menial jobs until he landed an executive position with an oil company. He married "the love of his life," a beautiful woman who was 17 years older than he. Marriage is like the newspaper, he said. "It had to be made fresh every damn day of every damn year." He put his writing career on hold until the 1930s. At first, he wrote crime fiction for pulp magazines whose readers demanded constant action. "If you stopped to think you were lost," he advised. "When in doubt have a man come through a door with a gun in his hand."

He schooled himself by reading Hemingway, Dreiser, and Lardner. He filled an address book with names and titles he liked and noted precise details of clothing and slang expressions. To force himself to put "a bit of magic" on every page, he wrote horizontally on small sheets of yellow paper, compressing his writing into just 12 to 15 lines to a page.

In 1938, he wrote his first novel, *The Big Sleep*, narrated by detective Philip Marlowe. Bitter and jaded by life, Marlowe battles the corruption of a dark and sinister world. Chandler wrote seven Philip Marlowe novels, which have sold into the millions and have been translated into more than 25 languages. Chandler's books and screenplays produced more than a dozen movies, inspired the classic *Chinatown*, and were instrumental in the birth of film noir.

Biographer Tom Hiney reports that 17 people attended Chandler's burial in "San Diego's Mount Hope state cemetery in plot number 1577-3-8." Chandler would have appreciated the lean prose and the exact detail.

Par for the Course

As sport, writing is a lot like golf: you compete, mostly alone, and largely against yourself, on a long course fraught with obstacles, in a game where perfection is in theory attainable but seldom achieved by even the most dogged practitioner.

It's little wonder that golf has spawned its own small genre of literature. From how-to manuals like Ben Hogan's *Five Lessons: The Modern Fundamentals of Golf* (1957), Jack Nicklaus's *Golf My Way* (1974), and Tom Watson's *Getting Up and Down* (1983), to Harvey Penick's minimalist 1990s series on the sport as spiritual undertaking, to John Updike's 1996 *Golf Dreams*, the royal and ancient game has long driven those addicted to it to write. "Golf," Updike believes, "inspires as much verbiage as astrology."

Some years ago, former *Esquire* editor Lee Eisenberg spent an entire winter reading golf books in an effort, he said, "to divine how to launch a golf ball long and true." He concluded that there are three fundamental kinds of books on the sport: instruction manuals, psychological guides (Timothy Gallwey's 1979 best-seller, *The Inner Game of Golf*, is exemplary), and works that purport to reflect on golf's deeper meanings and "ineffable hold on the spirit." In the last category, Michael Murphy's *Golf in the Kingdom* (1972), a mystical account of an evening spent on a wind-swept course by the North Sea, is emblematic.

A handful of these books, as Eisenberg discovered, "made good on their promise to enlighten and instruct, but many proved fairly useless, accomplishing little more than to contribute to that infernal static filling the duffer's head whenever he contemplates a sidehill lie or cringes in the face of a greenside bunker."

Reporter John Feinstein, who has memorably described golf as "a good walk spoiled," knows better than most how trying the sport can be—particularly at its loftiest levels. He has written about the PGA tour, about Tiger Woods' messianic climb to the top, and about golf's "holy grail," its four major tournaments.

"No game is more imprecise, more elusive," Feinstein writes, in a passage that might serve equally to describe the writer's trade. "The greatest players alive wake up most mornings having no idea whether the day will produce a 65 or a 75. If they have a gut feeling, it will be wrong nine times out of ten."

Sunday

28

Beatrix Potter, b. 1866   Gerard Manley Hopkins, b. 1844

Monday

29

Booth Tarkington, b. 1869

Tuesday

30

Giorgio Vasari, b. 1511   Emily Brontë, b. 1818

Wednesday

31

 Thursday

1

Herman Melville, b. 1819

Friday

2

James Baldwin, b. 1924

Saturday

3

Rupert Brooke, b. 1887

July						
S	M	T	W	T	F	S
	1	2	3	4	5	6
7	8	9	10	11	12	13
14	15	16	17	18	19	20
21	22	23	24	25	26	27
28	29	30	31			

July/August
2002

August						
S	M	T	W	T	F	S
				1	2	3
4	5	6	7	8	9	10
11	12	13	14	15	16	17
18	19	20	21	22	23	24
25	26	27	28	29	30	31

Sunday
4

W.H. Hudson, b. 1841   Knut Hamsun, b. 1859

Monday
5

Tuesday
6

François Fénelon, b. 1651   Alfred Lord Tennyson, b. 1809

Wednesday
7

Thursday
8

Marjorie Kinnan Rawlings, b. 1896   Sara Teasdale, b. 1884

Friday
9

P.L. Travers, b. 1899

Saturday
10

August						
S	M	T	W	T	F	S
				1	2	3
4	5	6	7	8	9	10
11	12	13	14	15	16	17
18	19	20	21	22	23	24
25	26	27	28	29	30	31

August
2002

September						
S	M	T	W	T	F	S
1	2	3	4	5	6	7
8	9	10	11	12	13	14
15	16	17	18	19	20	21
22	23	24	25	26	27	28
29	30					

François Fénelon
August 6, 1651 – January 7, 1715

In the last year of his life, beset by chronic poor health and decades of political and religious turmoil, the writer, former royal tutor, and archbishop François Fénelon described himself as "only a skeleton who walks and talks, who sleeps and eats but little." The world, he confessed to a correspondent, was "full of thorns, troubles, and of odious, deceptive, and dastardly dealings."

It had been so for most of his life. Except in his first years as a priest, when he knew a "life of pure spirituality," Fénelon drew fire at nearly every turn. His written defense of Quietism—a form of mysticism that believes the soul capable of passively attaining God's grace—led to papal censure and ultimately to

Fénelon's dismissal from the French court, where he had taught Louis XIV's son.

It was during his tenure as the Dauphin's tutor that Fénelon wrote his best-known work, the *Télémaque*. Fénelon had long believed in the power of stories, fairy tales, and fables (of which he wrote 36) to edify and instruct the young. He described his *Télémaque* as "a fabulous narrative in the form of a heroic poem, like those written by Homer and Virgil, into which I incorporated the major lessons suitable for a prince who by virtue of his birth is destined to reign."

Profoundly inspired by ancient sources, the *Télémaque* recounts the adventures of Ulysses' son, and in the process denounces the affectations of a materialistic existence. Nature and simplicity are to be cultivated, Fénelon argues. Suffering teaches compassion for the less fortunate. "Those who have never suffered know nothing; they are unacquainted with either good or evil; they do not know men; they do not know themselves."

Against Fénelon's will, the *Télémaque* was published in 1699 and reportedly sold 600 copies in one day. Many deemed it a satire on Louis XIV and his ostentatious regime. The king ordered the work confiscated, and Fénelon was prohibited from ever again communicating with members of the court.

He ended his days in exile in Cambrai, in northeastern France, where he ministered to the local population through famine, war, and the routine hardships of life in the first years of the 18th century. He continued to write, and although he never actively sought to publish, his works eventually found their way into print, where they attest to Fénelon's maxim: "The true use of eloquence [is] to publish truth."

T. E. Lawrence
August 16, 1888 – May 19, 1935

Originally, Theodore Edward Lawrence planned to use the title of his most famous work, *Seven Pillars of Wisdom*, for a travel book on seven eastern cities. Ever the perfectionist, however, Lawrence abandoned that effort (he later claimed to have burned the manuscript) and applied the title to his now-legendary account of his military activities in the Middle East during World War I.

By late 1919, Lawrence had nearly completed a first draft of the celebrated book when he lost his only copy of the work, along with photographs, negatives, and most of his notes for the last chapters, in a train station. Friends persuaded him to rewrite the volume from memory, a feat he completed by mid-1920.

One of five illegitimate sons born to a Welsh gentleman and a former governess, Lawrence was, and remained, a man of shifting identities. He said he neither understood himself nor wanted to. His biographer Robert Graves claimed that Lawrence "fought coherence. I could not, and cannot do for him what he has set his face against doing for himself."

At Oxford, Lawrence studied modern history and wrote a thesis on medieval Syrian castles. Urged to publish the work, Lawrence demurred, calling it "an elementary performance…not worth printing."

He longed to be a great writer and spent hours refining his sentences and paragraphs. George Bernard Shaw called him "one of the greatest descriptive writers in English literature." Witness the precision of Lawrence's language in the opening passage of *Seven Pillars*: "For years we lived anyhow with one another in the naked desert, under the indifferent heaven. By day the hot sun fermented us; and we were dizzied by the beating wind. At night we were stained by dew, and shamed into pettiness by the innumerable silences of stars."

Seven Pillars recalls the two years Lawrence spent as a British Army officer working with Arab troops in their revolt against the Turks. Long before the book was published, journalists had pounced on the romance of Lawrence's desert adventures, and to his dismay, he became a world celebrity. David Lean's 1962 film, *Lawrence of Arabia*, merely sealed that fate.

Despite his insistence that *Seven Pillars* was "longwinded and pretentious, and dull," "a stodgy mess of mock-heroic egotism," its author—who died at age 46 from injuries sustained in a motorcycle accident—is one of the great prose stylists of his time. The book is a modern classic.

Sunday

11

Louise Bogan, b. 1897

Monday

12

Madame Blavatsky, b. 1831   Edith Hamilton, b. 1867   Mary Roberts Rinehart, b. 1876

Tuesday

13

Wednesday

14

 Thursday

15

Louise Colet, b. 1810   Edna Ferber, b. 1855   Sir Walter Scott, b. 1771   Thomas De Quincey, b. 1785

Friday

16

T. E. Lawrence, b. 1888

Saturday

17

Ted Hughes, b. 1930   Mae West, b. 1893

August						
S	M	T	W	T	F	S
				1	2	3
4	5	6	7	8	9	10
11	12	13	14	15	16	17
18	19	20	21	22	23	24
25	26	27	28	29	30	31

**August
2002**

September						
S	M	T	W	T	F	S
1	2	3	4	5	6	7
8	9	10	11	12	13	14
15	16	17	18	19	20	21
22	23	24	25	26	27	28
29	30					

Sunday
18

Elsa Morante, b. 1918

Monday
19

Ogden Nash, b. 1902

Tuesday
20

H.P. Lovecraft, b. 1890

Wednesday
21

Thursday
22

Dorothy Parker, b. 1893

Friday
23

Edgar Lee Masters, b. 1868

Saturday
24

Max Beerbohm, b. 1872   *Jorge Luis Borges, b. 1899*

August 2002

August						
S	M	T	W	T	F	S
					1	2	3
4	5	6	7	8	9	10
11	12	13	14	15	16	17
18	19	20	21	22	23	24
25	26	27	28	29	30	31

September						
S	M	T	W	T	F	S
1	2	3	4	5	6	7
8	9	10	11	12	13	14
15	16	17	18	19	20	21
22	23	24	25	26	27	28
29	30					

Max Beerbohm
August 24, 1872 – May 20, 1956

George Bernard Shaw dubbed him "The Incomparable Max." "He is not incomparable at all," Vita Sackville-West said crossly. "He is a shallow, affected, self-conscious fribble—so there."

Max "has the most remarkable and seductive genius," Lytton Strachey observed, "and I should say about the smallest in the world." A small man with a large moustache, Beerbohm agreed with them all. "My gifts are small," he wrote. "I've used them very well and discreetly, never straining them; and the result is that I've made a charming little reputation."

His reputation rests on one classic novel, *Zuleika Dobson* (1911), his delightful caricatures, a collection of stories, and many witty essays. In 1896, when he was just 23, he compiled 7 of the 16 essays he had written and published them as *The Works of Max Beerbohm with a Bibliography by John Lane.*

"In essay writing," Beerbohm explained, "style is everything. The essayist's aim is to bring himself home to his reader, to express himself in exact terms. Therefore, he must find exact words for his thoughts, and cadences which express the very tone of his emotions." In his essay *A Defence of Cosmetics,* Beerbohm noted, "Most women are not so young as they are painted." In conversation, his wit could be biting. William Morris was "a wonderful all-round man," he told S.N. Behrman, "but the act of walking round him has always tired me."

Beerbohm took over Shaw's position as drama critic for the *Saturday Review*, but in writing criticism, he lacked Shaw's creativity and discriminating genius. "When I am praising anyone," Beerbohm sighed, "I am always deadly dull."

In 1910, Beerbohm married the actress Florence Kahn. They settled in Rapallo, Italy, where they lived for the rest of their lives. For years, young writers stopped at his Villino Chiaro to pay their respects to the "incomparable Max."

He was knighted in 1939. On his 70th birthday, he expressed amazement that he had flourished both in the 19th and 20th centuries. "I regard myself as the smallest success of both," he said. He claimed that he had never really liked the grim labor of writing. He attributed his success to the affection of his family, "to an immensely happy marriage, and to the kindness of a host of friends."

He died peacefully at his home in Rapallo. His ashes were sent to London and buried in St. Paul's Cathedral.

Marguerite Young
August 26, 1908 – November 17, 1995

Years ago, while in the midst of work on a novel that was going badly, Anne Tyler dipped into Marguerite Young's gargantuan, 1,198-page novel, *Miss MacIntosh, My Darling*. "Whatever page I turned to, it seemed, a glorious wealth of words swooped out at me," Tyler recalled. "I always went back to my own book feeling more hopeful, more aware of possibilities." In tribute to Young's work, Tyler gave *Miss MacIntosh* as a "traveling companion" to the hero of her novel *The Accidental Tourist*.

It is generally acknowledged that few have actually read *Miss MacIntosh*, let alone read it in its entirety. Hailed as "one of the most widely unread books ever acclaimed," Young's one and only novel earned both raves and jeers in its time, but even the book's fiercest admirers—among them Anaïs Nin, Djuna Barnes, and John Gardner—concede that it is best savored one piece at a time, like bon-bons in a dish.

Young became a legend after Scribner published *Miss MacIntosh* in 1965. Dressed in her signature serapes, with a pageboy haircut that underscored her resemblance to W.H. Auden, she strolled through Greenwich Village by day and night, breakfasting with Richard Wright, getting drunk with Dylan Thomas, and regaling friends with tales of her romantic conquests. (She claimed to have welcomed Allen Tate's advances but to have shunned those of Carson McCullers. "Well, Carson, if I could love any woman, it would be you," she said.)

Precocious from birth, she wrote her first poems at six, joined the Authors League at 11, published her first poem at 19, and her first book, the poetry collection *Prismatic Ground*, at 28, one year after receiving a master's degree in Elizabethan and Jacobean literature from the University of Chicago.

During her student days in Chicago she took a part-time job reading to a wealthy addict, Minna Weissenbach, whose astonishing flights of drug-induced fancy later inspired the celebrated "opium lady" of Young's *Miss MacIntosh*.

Young herself disdained drugs but embraced fantasy. Ever unorthodox, she dreamt up a far more interesting world than the one that surrounded her in real life. In the mid-1980s she told an interviewer that she regularly saw Emily Dickinson, Virginia Woolf, and Charles Dickens in the Village. And "Poe, oh, all the time. I see him on misty nights at Sheridan Square when the rain's falling. He's going into a little cigar store to get a cigar. I am on very close terms with Poe."

Sunday
25

Bret Harte, b. 1836

Monday
26

Julio Cortázar, b. 1914
Zona Gale, b. 1874   Marguerite Young, b. 1908   Late Summer Holiday (U.K. ex. Scotland)

Tuesday
27

Theodore Dreiser, b. 1871

Wednesday
28

Robertson Davies, b. 1913   Johann Wolfgang Goethe, b. 1749

Thursday
29

Maurice Maeterlinck, b. 1862

 Friday
30

Mary Wollstonecraft Shelley, b. 1797

Saturday
31

William Saroyan, b. 1908   William Shawn, b. 1907

August						
S	M	T	W	T	F	S
				1	2	3
4	5	6	7	8	9	10
11	12	13	14	15	16	17
18	19	20	21	22	23	24
25	26	27	28	29	30	31

August
2002

September						
S	M	T	W	T	F	S
1	2	3	4	5	6	7
8	9	10	11	12	13	14
15	16	17	18	19	20	21
22	23	24	25	26	27	28
29	30					

Sunday

1

Edgar Rice Burroughs, b. 1875

Monday

2

Labor Day

Tuesday

3

Sarah Orne Jewett, b. 1849

Wednesday

4

Antonin Artaud, b. 1896   Craig Claiborne, b. 1920   Mary Renault, b. 1905   Richard Wright, b. 1908

Thursday

5

Friday

6

Rosh Hashanah begins at sunset, Hebrew year 5763

Saturday

7

Elinor Wylie, b. 1885

September						
S	M	T	W	T	F	S
1	2	3	4	5	6	7
8	9	10	11	12	13	14
15	16	17	18	19	20	21
22	23	24	25	26	27	28
29	30					

September
2002

October						
S	M	T	W	T	F	S
		1	2	3	4	5
6	7	8	9	10	11	12
13	14	15	16	17	18	19
20	21	22	23	24	25	26
27	28	29	30	31		

Craig Claiborne
September 4, 1920 – January 22, 2000

He believed that the ability to write well and the ability to taste were instinctive, born not made. But what if he had grown up in a home without a love of food? In his parents' boarding house in the Mississippi Delta, Claiborne ate the best of southern cooking—fried chicken, beaten biscuits, pecan pie, and coconut cake with meringue and fresh coconut topping.

Eventually, Claiborne became totally estranged from his dominating mother, but he never shook free of her culinary influence. Years later, the aroma of chopped onions, celery, green pepper, and minced garlic could transport him instantly into her kitchen.

After attending Mississippi State, Claiborne graduated from the University of Missouri with a degree in journalism. In 1942, he joined the Navy and enjoyed a "glorious war." He drank his first wine and tasted family-style French cooking—roast chicken and omelets and salads with *sauce vinaigrette* and tarts filled with pastry cream.

After the war, he attended a hotel school in Lausanne, Switzerland and learned lessons that he carried with him into his restaurant criticism. "Nothing is more vulgar," he was taught, "than an excess of food on a plate."

In 1957, the *New York Times* hired him as the first male food editor as well as restaurant critic. "He came at just the right time," said Julia Child. "There was no real restaurant reviewing until he came along." He visited restaurants anonymously, wrote intelligent and rigorous reviews, and earned the respect of his readers and restaurateurs alike. At Le Pavillon, Claiborne met the chef, Pierre Franey, and the two began a friendship and a collaboration that resulted in seven books, including the best-selling *The New York Times Cook Book.*

On his 70th birthday, Claiborne wined and dined at a garden party in Monte Carlo on specialties brought by 60 chefs from around the world. "It was without question the greatest day of my life," he said.

Claiborne made fine cooking accessible to ordinary people. Since he was also one of the first to publicize the benefits of a low-fat, low-salt diet with *Craig Claiborne's Gourmet Diet* (1980), perhaps he saved some lives as well.

Although he never considered himself a great writer, writing for him was as essential and as necessary as food. "I write because I have to write," he said, "not only as a source of income but because of some inexplicable physical and mental need."

Jessica Mitford
September 11, 1917 – July 23, 1996

The novelist and biographer Nancy Mitford
once told a reporter, "Sisters stand between
one and life's cruel circumstances." Jessica
Mitford disagreed. "Sisters—and especially
Nancy," she said, *were* life's cruel circumstances."

As the youngest of seven in an eccentric,
upper-class British family, Jessica Mitford
literally ran away from her life and wrote
herself a new one. Since her parents didn't
believe in sending their daughters to school,
Jessica was educated at home. Jessica had
nothing in common with her sister, Unity,
who decorated her side of the room with
swastikas, Nazi pennants, and photographs of Hitler. In retaliation, Jessica displayed
her bust of Lenin, stacks of *Daily Worker*s, and carved hammers and sickles in the
windows.

At 19, Mitford eloped with Esmond Romilly, a communist sympathizer and nephew of
Winston Churchill. She was immediately disinherited by her father. The couple moved
to the United States, and in 1941, Romilly, who had joined the Canadian Air Force,
was killed in action. To support herself, Mitford took a series of jobs, including
bartending, union organizing, and clerking. In 1943, she married Robert Treuhaft, a
labor lawyer, and they moved to Oakland, California, where they joined the Communist Party.

Figuring that "the only thing that requires no education and no skills is writing," she
decided to become a writer when she was 38. Her autobiography, *Daughters and
Rebels*, earned her respect and accolades, but her next book, *The American Way of
Death*, created a sensation. With scathing humor and impeccable research, Mitford
revealed the high cost of dying. She reported that the greedy funeral industry was
perpetrating a "huge, macabre and expensive practical joke on the American public,"
and she poked fun at euphemisms which turned undertakers into "funeral directors"
and corpses into "loved ones."

In later works, she investigated corruption in television, fat farms, prisons, and
medicine. *Time* magazine dubbed her the "Queen of the Muckrakers." Her articles are
collected in *Poison Penmanship: The Gentle Art of Muckraking*. "You may not be able
to change the world," she said, "but at least you can embarrass the guilty."

Mitford died of cancer at 78. She had joked that she wanted an elaborate, expensive
funeral with six black horses and "one of those marvelous jobs of embalming that take
20 years off." Instead, practical and irreverent to the end, she arranged for a $475
cremation.

Sunday

8

Joaquin Miller, b. 1837

Monday

9

Leo Tolstoy, b. 1828

Tuesday

10

Hilda Doolittle, (H.D.), b. 1886

Wednesday

11

O. Henry, b. 1862   D.H. Lawrence, b. 1885   Jessica Mitford, b. 1917

Thursday

12

Anna Cora Mowatt, b. 1819

 Friday

13

Emily Haven, b. 1827   Roald Dahl, b. 1916

Saturday

14

September						
S	M	T	W	T	F	S
1	2	3	4	5	6	7
8	9	10	11	12	13	14
15	16	17	18	19	20	21
22	23	24	25	26	27	28
29	30					

September
2002

October						
S	M	T	W	T	F	S
		1	2	3	4	5
6	7	8	9	10	11	12
13	14	15	16	17	18	19
20	21	22	23	24	25	26
27	28	29	30	31		

Sunday

15

Yom Kippur begins at sunset   *Agatha Christie, b. 1890   James Fenimore Cooper, b. 1789*

Monday

16

Emilia Pardo Bazán, b. 1851   Henry St. John, Viscount Bolingbroke, b. 1678

Tuesday

17

U.S. Constitution adopted, 1787   *Emile Augier, b. 1820   William Carlos Williams, b. 1883*

Wednesday

18

Samuel Johnson, b. 1709

Thursday

19

Friday

20

Stevie Smith, b. 1902   Upton Sinclair, b. 1879

Saturday

21

September						
S	M	T	W	T	F	S
1	2	3	4	5	6	7
8	9	10	11	12	13	14
15	16	17	18	19	20	21
22	23	24	25	26	27	28
29	30					

September
2002

October						
S	M	T	W	T	F	S
		1	2	3	4	5
6	7	8	9	10	11	12
13	14	15	16	17	18	19
20	21	22	23	24	25	26
27	28	29	30	31		

Emile Augier
September 17, 1820 – October 25, 1889

The theater in mid-19th century France was an enormously popular industry, and Emile Augier was one of France's most prolific, most successful playwrights. In 1853, when he received a bad review of a play, he challenged the critic to a duel. Both men emerged unscathed from the encounter.

Throughout his long career, Augier wasn't afraid to take on the press, the clergy, politicians, or corrupt aristocrats. He believed that the theater could be a powerful force for social change and wanted his plays to reflect contemporary social life. At a time when the bourgeoisie was merging with the aristocracy, Augier's characters demonstrated that love could bridge the social divide.

His middle-class parents hoped that he would become a lawyer and Augier earned a law degree from the University of Paris. Like his idol, Molière, Augier turned his back on the law to devote himself to writing. Along with his contemporary Dumas *fils*, Augier rejected romanticism and wrote plays about current social issues. His well-crafted scripts about sex, money, and power reflected (and, some critics say, pandered to) the interests of his middle-class audience.

Unlike Molière's plays, however, Augier's works are dated and are rarely performed today. In his satire *The Impoverished Lionesses*, he wrote about how greed could turn a good woman into a kept woman, all because she desired an elegant hat. After Dumas *fils'* huge success with *The Lady of the Camellias*, about a prostitute who finds true love, Augier attacked the idea that a prostitute could be rehabilitated. In *The Marriage of Olympia*, to save his family's honor, a Marquis kills the prostitute who has married his nephew and then is himself condemned to death.

On the other hand, Augier sympathized with women. "Work, which is man's glory, makes a declassée of woman," he wrote. "The world is ever on its guard against a woman who wants to make an honest living. Her path is difficult, and all society is waiting to see her make a false step."

Augier never seemed to take a false step during his illustrious career. His gift for clever dialogue, compelling characters, and his themes—crime doesn't pay, greed is bad, marriage vows should be honored, a good father should recognize his illegitimate son, and love conquers all—made him enormously popular with audiences, critics, and peers. At 38, he was elected without opposition to the *Academie Française*. In 1878, he retired, a well-beloved and venerated literary statesman.

Confucius
ca. 551 – 479 B.C.E.

The ruthless men who held power in his native state of Lu (now Shandong province, China) had no taste for the blunt criticisms that Confucius leveled against their cruel regimes. "If this man can be endured, who cannot be endured!" he said of one local leader. Another ruler was advised to steer clear of Confucius because the philosopher was "impractical, conceited, set a high value on ceremony, and had many peculiarities."

Little is known about the visionary man whose thoughts on politics, education, and social reform were to shape Chinese—and, indeed, East Asian—civilization for upwards of 2,000 years. Having lost his father in early childhood, he was raised by his mother in humble circumstances. Poverty, he said, gave him practical experience of simple, everyday matters that were beneath the notice of the noble-born.

At 15, he resolved to devote his "heart" to learning. At the time, books were cumbersome objects, composed by means of a stylus on bamboo strips that were subsequently bound together with leather thongs. In all likelihood, Confucius encountered them in the offices of the state administration, where he was briefly employed in a minor post. At 19, he married; he fathered a son and daughter.

"To learn, and not to think over [what one has learnt] is useless," Confucius believed. His own learning evolved into a system of principles that attracted as many as 70 disciples, men who willingly followed Confucius on a ten-year quest to find a ruler who would adopt his ideas on government, men who recorded and later disseminated his teachings through such works as the *Analects* and the *Book of Changes (I Ching)*.

The goal for each individual, Confucius said, is to develop our personality until we achieve the ideal of a perfect human, a sage. Central to this pursuit are the virtues of compassion, courtesy, love, goodness, benevolence, kindness, and human-heartedness.

That Confucius could find no ruler to take up his cause is not surprising, given the bellicose nature of the age. It was not until the start of the Han Dynasty, some 200 years after his death, that his teachings became widely accepted.

His disciples remembered him as a humane, lovable person of exceptional height and great dignity, who loved music, dance, and outdoor sports. His greatest passion, however, was education. "I have never grown tired of learning," he declared.

Sunday

22

Monday

23

Fall Equinox, 12:56 am EDT

Tuesday

24

Horace Walpole, b. 1717   F. Scott Fitzgerald, b. 1896   Frances Ellen Watkins Harper, b. 1825 [?]

Wednesday

25

Red Smith, b.1905   William Faulkner, b. 1897

Thursday

26

T.S. Eliot, b. 1888

Friday

27

Grazia Deledda, b. 1871

Saturday

28

September						
S	M	T	W	T	F	S
1	2	3	4	5	6	7
8	9	10	11	12	13	14
15	16	17	18	19	20	21
22	23	24	25	26	27	28
29	30					

September
2002

October						
S	M	T	W	T	F	S
		1	2	3	4	5
6	7	8	9	10	11	12
13	14	15	16	17	18	19
20	21	22	23	24	25	26
27	28	29	30	31		

Sunday
29

Monday
30

Tuesday
1

Wednesday
2

Thursday
3

Friday
4

Saturday
5

September						
S	M	T	W	T	F	S
1	2	3	4	5	6	7
8	9	10	11	12	13	14
15	16	17	18	19	20	21
22	23	24	25	26	27	28
29	30					

September/ October 2002

October						
S	M	T	W	T	F	S
		1	2	3	4	5
6	7	8	9	10	11	12
13	14	15	16	17	18	19
20	21	22	23	24	25	26
27	28	29	30	31		

Roy Campbell
October 2, 1901 – April 23, 1957

In his poem "The Making of a Poet," Roy Campbell wrote, "In every herd there is some restive steer / who leaps the cows and heads each hot stampede."

As a boy growing up in Durban, South Africa, Campbell escaped the confined parochialism of his hometown. Southern Africa was wild and untamed, and Campbell hunted wild game in Rhodesia, fished in the sea, and rode horseback through the bush around Durban. He also sketched, wrote verse, and immersed himself in a study of poetry, especially Baudelaire.

At 17, he left Durban to study at Oxford University. He stayed less than a year, but he met Wyndham Lewis, T.S. Eliot and Edith Sitwell. After leaving Oxford, he lived in Provence and worked as a deckhand on coastal ships. Against his father's wishes, in 1922 he married Mary Garman. His father cut off his allowance and the couple moved to North Wales. While living in a converted stable in Wales, Campbell wrote *The Flaming Terrapin*, a long narrative poem retelling the story of the Flood and Noah's Ark, and created a sensation.

After his success, Campbell moved back to South Africa, where he started a literary magazine that championed racial equality. The financial backer withdrew support, Campbell resigned and returned to England. He vented his anger in a long poem, *The Wayzgoose*, which satirized "South Africa, renowned both far and wide / For politics and little else beside." In his next poem, *The Georgiad* (1931), he attacked the Bloomsbury Group: "Write with your spade, and garden with your pen / Shovel your couplets to their long repose / And type your turnips down the field in rows."

During the Spanish Civil War, Campbell fought for Franco and the Nationalists, yet paradoxically, he later wrote *Lorca: An Appreciation of His Poetry*, which demonstrated his remarkable affinity for the poetry of Franco's most famous victim.

A boastful, swaggering man, Campbell piloted gliders and fought bulls, yet he had a quiet, mystical side as well and in addition to his own poetry, he published brilliant translations of French and Spanish writers, including his highly-praised work *The Poems of St. John of the Cross*. A dedicated artist, Campbell once told his friend David Wright, "I place friendship above art."

A few months before his death in an automobile accident in Portugal, wearing a black Cordoba over his white hair, the poet strode into a London pub. Then, David Wright recalled, "an extraordinary thing happened: everyone in the pub spontaneously rose to his feet."

Eugenio Montale
October 12, 1896 – September 12, 1981

By rights, Eugenio Montale should have slipped into a quiet old age, the respected author of three collections of poetry: *Ossi di seppia* (Cuttlefish Bones, 1925), *Le occasioni* (The Occasions, 1939), and *La bufera e altro* (The Storm and Other Poems, 1956). His decidedly unprolific output gave no reason to expect more.

But in 1971, at age 75, Montale abruptly published a hefty collection of new poems. Two years later he issued *Diario del '71 e del '72* (Diary of '71 and '72), and in 1977 he released *Quaderno di quattro anni* (Notebook of Four Years). A 1980 edition of Montale's complete works contained even further novelties, including a complete verse collection. Meanwhile, a rejuvenated Montale took home the 1975 Nobel Prize for Literature.

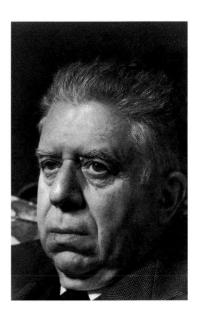

His first love was bel canto, which he studied briefly in his teens. But his teacher's sudden death sapped "the magic, if not song itself," from the exercise, and Montale turned to words. Music continued to inform both his life and his writing. A gifted baritone who occasionally treated close friends to private concerts, Montale spoke of poetry's "common parentage with music." "There exists a problem of pitch even outside of singing, in every human enterprise," he said.

From 1955 to 1967, Montale earned his living as a music critic in Milan. He reportedly attended every La Scala opening. Although he disparaged journalism as "a grind for grub," he hailed the effect that its constant discipline had on his poetry.

At one point, Montale took up painting as a hobby, using wine, coffee grounds, toothpaste, and cigarette ashes to blend his colors. His writing tools were just as shabby: instead of good paper, Montale preferred to write poetry on bus tickets and candy wrappers.

By nature a loner, Montale married once and in poetry invoked his own, 20th-century Beatrice, the American Dante scholar Irma Brandeis, whom Montale dubbed "Clizia." He opposed Fascism during World War II, but did not join the Italian Resistance. Criticized for his refusal to act, he responded, "I have lived my time with the minimum of cowardice that was allowed to my weak powers, but there are those who did more, much more, even if they did not publish books."

About poetry, he was similarly guarded. "It is an entity," he said in his Nobel speech, "about which we know quite little."

 *Sunday*
6

Caroline Gordon, b. 1895

Monday
7

Tuesday
8

Wednesday
9

Bruce Catton, b. 1899

Thursday
10

Ken Saro-Wiwa, b. 1941   Ivan Bunin, b. 1870

Friday
11

François Mauriac, b. 1885   Eleanor Roosevelt, b. 1884

Saturday
12

Eugenio Montale, b. 1896

October						
S	M	T	W	T	F	S
		1	2	3	4	5
6	7	8	9	10	11	12
13	14	15	16	17	18	19
20	21	22	23	24	25	26
27	28	29	30	31		

October
2002

November						
S	M	T	W	T	F	S
					1	2
3	4	5	6	7	8	9
10	11	12	13	14	15	16
17	18	19	20	21	22	23
24	25	26	27	28	29	30

Sunday
13

Monday
14

Hannah Arendt, b. 1906
Katherine Mansfield, b. 1888   e.e. cummings, b. 1894

Tuesday
15

Friedrich Nietzsche, b. 1844   Virgil, b. 70 B.C.   P.G. Wodehouse, b. 1881

Wednesday
16

Oscar Wilde, b. 1854   Eugene O'Neill, b. 1888   Noah Webster, b. 1758

Thursday
17

Elinor Glyn, b. 1864

Friday
18

Saturday
19
Fannie Hurst, b. 1889

\	\	October	\	\	\	\
S	M	T	W	T	F	S
		1	2	3	4	5
6	7	8	9	10	11	12
13	14	15	16	17	18	19
20	21	22	23	24	25	26
27	28	29	30	31		

October
2002

\	\	November	\	\	\	\
S	M	T	W	T	F	S
					1	2
3	4	5	6	7	8	9
10	11	12	13	14	15	16
17	18	19	20	21	22	23
24	25	26	27	28	29	30

Friedrich Nietzsche
October 15, 1844 – August 25, 1900

On January 8, 1889, in Piazza Carlo Alberto in Turin, a coachman brutally whipped his horse. Friedrich Nietzsche, then 44, saw the ugly scene. Sobbing, Nietzsche wrapped his arms around the horse's neck and collapsed into insanity. The German philosopher-poet would never know that his work, written in the 19th century, would profoundly influence subsequent philosophers.

Today, widely quoted and enormously popular, Nietzsche was in his own time largely unknown. After his death, his sister and literary executor Elisabeth, who had married an anti-Semite, deliberately forged and manipulated Nietzsche's writings and ideas. His philosophy was further distorted by Nazi propagandists. Years of scholarly work and new translations have cleared away the lies and misrepresentations, and Nietzsche has achieved what he had prophesied. "My time has not yet come either; some are born posthumously."

His grandfather and father were Lutheran ministers, and Nietzsche was expected to follow in the family tradition. When Friedrich was four, his father died of a brain disease, and the boy was raised in a house of women. At ten, the boy wrote what he called "terrible" poetry, had a passion for knowledge, and loved "to sing Biblical texts to a fantastic accompaniment on the piano." Later, he believed that the death of his father had "planted the seeds of earnestness and contemplation in my soul."

From 1864 to 1868, Nietzsche studied philology in Bonn and Leipzig, earning a doctorate from the University of Leipzig. In 1869 he became a professor of classics in Basel, Switzerland. A year later he wrote a friend, "Scholarship, art, and philosophy have grown together in me to such a point that I'm sure to give birth to centaurs." Two years later, he published *The Birth of Tragedy*, which outlined his theory of the Apollonian-Dionysian dichotomy.

In 1879, Nietzsche retired from teaching and during the next ten years wrote *Thus Spake Zarathustra, Beyond Good and Evil,* and *On the Genealogy of Morals.* Nietzsche had an unusual, aphoristic style and wanted to "say in ten sentences what everyone else…does *not* say in a whole book." Nietzsche railed against conformism and nationalism, ripped away the pieties of conventional morality, and challenged Christianity, asking, "Is man only a blunder of God, or God only a blunder of man?"

After his breakdown in January 1889, Nietzsche posed no more philosophical questions and lived the rest of his life in mental darkness. "And if you gaze for long into an abyss," he had written earlier, "the abyss gazes also into you."

Sarah Josepha Hale
October 24, 1788 – April 30, 1879

Although most people think it's a Mother Goose rhyme, "Mary's Lamb" (aka "Mary Had a Little Lamb") is actually the work of Sarah Josepha Hale, writer, editor, and crusader for issues as disparate as childhood education, the moral superiority of women, housekeeping as a "domestic science," the construction of monuments to commemorate Bunker Hill and Mt. Vernon, and the creation of Thanksgiving Day. On the matters of Bunker Hill, Mt. Vernon, and Thanksgiving, she prevailed. On October 3, 1863, Abraham Lincoln proclaimed Thanksgiving a national American holiday.

From her New England mother, a woman Hale described as having possessed the "uncommon advantages of education for a female of her times," Sarah learned "serious truth" couched in charming stories, songs, and legends—a practice she passed on to her own children, and one she sought to formalize in America's schools.

She earned the equivalent of a college degree by studying informally with her brother Horatio, a Dartmouth student. In 1813, she married lawyer David Hale, with whom she studied nightly, "from eight o'clock in the evening till ten." This progressive arrangement ended after nine years when David Hale died, leaving 34-year-old Sarah pregnant with their fifth child and in dire need of employment.

After a short stint as a milliner, Hale turned to writing. In 1827 she published *Northwood*, a study of contrasts between the American North and South, and coincidentally the first American novel by a woman. The book also came out in England. Hale's newfound prestige led to an invitation to edit the Boston-based *Ladies' Magazine*, intended as "the first magazine edited by a woman for women."

Ten years later, Hale became the editor of *Godey's Lady's Book*, billed as "the mirror of woman's mind." She retained the post for the next 41 years. One of the most successful publications of the 19th century, *Godey's* offered sewing patterns, recipes, house plans, columns on domestic concerns, and both poetry and prose. At Hale's insistence, the magazine published only American authors.

Her advice to writers was succinct: they should write as they "would speak. They imagine they must have a lofty theme, and long words and pompous descriptions. We never read such."

Hale died at 89, just 16 months after resigning from *Godey's*. In her final column to readers, she voiced her "heartfelt prayer" that American women would continue to find "new avenues for higher culture and for good works."

Sunday
20

Arthur Rimbaud, b. 1854   Sukkot begins at sunset

Monday
21

Samuel Taylor Coleridge, b. 1772

Tuesday
22

Wednesday
23

Thursday
24

Moss Hart, b. 1904   *Sarah Josepha Hale, b. 1788*

Friday
25

Harold Brodkey, b. 1930

Saturday
26

Beryl Markham, b. 1902   *Sylvia Plath, b. 1932*   *Dylan Thomas, b. 1914*

October						
S	M	T	W	T	F	S
		1	2	3	4	5
6	7	8	9	10	11	12
13	14	15	16	17	18	19
20	21	22	23	24	25	26
27	28	29	30	31		

October
2002

November						
S	M	T	W	T	F	S
					1	2
3	4	5	6	7	8	9
10	11	12	13	14	15	16
17	18	19	20	21	22	23
24	25	26	27	28	29	30

Sunday
27
Daylight Saving Time ends   *Enid Bagnold, b. 1889   Evelyn Waugh, b. 1903*

Monday
28

James Boswell, b. 1740   Jean Giraudoux, b. 1882

Tuesday
29

Ezra Pound, b. 1885

Wednesday
30

Thursday
31

Halloween   *John Keats, b. 1795   Mary Wilkins Freeman, b. 1852*

Friday
1

Stephen Crane, b. 1871

Saturday
2

October						
S	M	T	W	T	F	S
	1	2	3	4	5
6	7	8	9	10	11	12
13	14	15	16	17	18	19
20	21	22	23	24	25	26
27	28	29	30	31		

October/ November 2002

November						
S	M	T	W	T	F	S
					1	2
3	4	5	6	7	8	9
10	11	12	13	14	15	16
17	18	19	20	21	22	23
24	25	26	27	28	29	30

Enid Bagnold
October 27, 1889 – March 31, 1981

As Lady Jones, the wife of Sir G. Roderick Jones, owner and director of Reuters News Agency, she didn't have to earn a living, but Enid Bagnold felt that writing was "the answer to everything." When she married, she stipulated that she must have three uninterrupted hours a day to write.

Born in Rochester, Kent, England, the daughter of a major in the Royal Engineers, Enid lived as a girl for three years in Jamaica. "This was the first page of my life as someone who can 'see'," she recalled. In Jamaica, she was allowed to wander freely, and it was there she developed her love for horses and first began to write poetry.

Educated at Prior's Field, a boarding school run by Julia Huxley, the mother of Aldous Huxley, Bagnold won a prize for her poetry. "Heady fame," she recalled. "The gods had come down to announce that the clown was the poet." Unlike many writers, Enid had good looks, parents who adored her and spoiled her, and the money and the freedom to lead the life she chose. As a young woman she moved to London to work. She met Frank Harris, Max Beerbohm and George Bernard Shaw; had a fling with a prince; and began to write for money. Her first book, *A Diary without Dates* (1918) about her experiences working as a nurse's aid, was called "one of the most moving books that the war has evoked."

Her sixth novel, *National Velvet* (1935), which was made into a movie starring Elizabeth Taylor and Mickey Rooney, is considered her masterpiece. During World War II, she began to write plays. Her best play, *The Chalk Garden*, about Laurel, a young girl; her governess Miss Madrigal; and Laurel's imperious grandmother Mrs. St. Maugham; received critical and audience acclaim. Critic Kenneth Tynan called it the "finest artificial comedy to have flowed from an English…pen since the death of Congreve."

Bagnold believed that talking about her writing technique "spilt the secret and took the gilt off." She admitted, though, that sometimes she got "sick of how well I write. I get sick of those two voices—the one that speaks first and the one that (instantaneous, overlapping) suggests the improvement."

She never stopped writing. "Remember this when you are 77," she told her granddaughter. "That nothing has lessened the ecstasy of walking with bare feet over the dew, between the shades of apple trees, down a slope to write in a little wooden studio at 8:45 in the morning."

Peter Weiss
November 8, 1916 –
May 10, 1982

"I did not want to belong to any race, ideal, city, or language," wrote Peter Weiss, "and I wanted to see strength in my detachment alone."

Early on, Weiss had learned to "never count on anything that lies in the future." The son of a wealthy textile manufacturer in Berlin, Weiss had a rootless youth. Forced into exile by Nazi persecution, his family lived in England, Switzerland, and Czechoslovakia before settling in Sweden.

A gifted artist, Weiss studied painting at the Academy of Art in Prague in 1937. In Prague, he met Hermann Hesse, who became a valuable mentor. The following year, he joined his family in Sweden. He took various jobs, including teaching art education and film theory classes and working as a common laborer. His fellow workers who drank and fought and passed out in a stupor could not understand "why I should sit writing in a notebook and sometimes sketched." Between 1952 and 1960, he made 14 short documentary films. About the same time, he began writing exclusively in German.

Disillusioned with politics and living in a world that seemed mad, Weiss began to write plays that reflected his own search for meaning. His two most popular and enduring plays are *The Persecution and Assassination of Marat as Performed by the Inmates of the Asylum of Charenton Under the Direction of the Marquis de Sade* (1964*)*, usually shortened to *Marat/Sade,* and *The Investigation (1965)*, based on the mass murders at Auschwitz.

Weiss collected boxes of data in researching his plays, but he also had a strong spiritual connection to his material. "Auschwitz is my township," he said. Peter Brook's controversial production of *Marat/Sade* starring Glenda Jackson as Charlotte Corday, Ian Richardson as Marat, and Patrick Magee as de Sade earned a Tony Award in 1965. *The Investigation* premiered simultaneously in 16 European countries. Ingmar Bergman directed a Swedish version that lasted five hours, and a two-hour version debuted on Broadway in 1966. Weiss's plays are disturbing and theatrical. Because of his use of documentary materials, "criticism is in a way irrelevant," wrote one reviewer. In Weiss's theater, the leading roles are "played by history and ideas."

The world may be a madhouse, Weiss believed, but he took a stand against madness. "I want my plays, my new kind of theater, to force the inmates to declare themselves."

Sunday
3

 Monday
4

Ivan Sergeyevich Turgenev, b. 1816   Will Rogers, b. 1879

Tuesday
5

Ida Tarbell, b. 1857   Election Day

Wednesday
6

James Jones, b. 1921   Ramadan begins

Thursday
7

Albert Camus, b. 1913

Friday
8

Margaret Mitchell, b. 1900   Peter Weiss, b. 1916

Saturday
9

Anne Sexton, b. 1928

November						
S	M	T	W	T	F	S
					1	2
3	4	5	6	7	8	9
10	11	12	13	14	15	16
17	18	19	20	21	22	23
24	25	26	27	28	29	30

November
2002

December						
S	M	T	W	T	F	S
1	2	3	4	5	6	7
8	9	10	11	12	13	14
15	16	17	18	19	20	21
22	23	24	25	26	27	28
29	30	31				

Sunday
10

Martin Luther, b. 1483

Monday
11

Veterans' Day
Remembrance Day (Canada)   *Feodor Dostoevsky, b. 1821*

Tuesday
12

Sor Juana Inés de la Cruz, b. 1651   Elizabeth Cady Stanton, b. 1815   Roland Barthes, b. 1915

Wednesday
13

Saint Augustine, b. 354   Lady Caroline Lamb, b. 1785

Thursday
14

Constance Rourke, b. 1885

Friday
15

Marianne Moore, b. 1887

Saturday
16

George S. Kaufman, b. 1889

November						
S	M	T	W	T	F	S
					1	2
3	4	5	6	7	8	9
10	11	12	13	14	15	16
17	18	19	20	21	22	23
24	25	26	27	28	29	30

November
2002

December						
S	M	T	W	T	F	S
1	2	3	4	5	6	7
8	9	10	11	12	13	14
15	16	17	18	19	20	21
22	23	24	25	26	27	28
29	30	31				

Martin Luther
November 10, 1483 – February 18, 1546

On October 31, 1517, Martin Luther, a 33-year-old monk, delivered his "Disputation on the Declaration Concerning the Power of Indulgences"—better known as his Ninety-five Theses—to Albrecht of Brandenburg, the archbishop of Mainz and the German elector. (A colleague later claimed that Luther nailed the theses to the door of the Castle Church in Wittenberg.) Luther's document called for a debate on the Catholic practice of selling indulgences. Few manuscripts have had such a lasting impact.

Luther's inflammatory act—together with the nearly 60,000 printed pages that constitute his remaining literary output during a 30-year career—ignited the Protestant Reformation and changed the course of human history.

Born a peasant, Luther retained a deep affection for the vernacular and an earthy delight in human folly. In an attack on one Duke Heinrich of Brunswick, Luther characterized his opponent as a devil, an archprostitute, and a harem guard, and argued that anyone who thought differently could "do it in your pants, and hang it around your neck, and make it into a sausage, then gobble it down like the gross asses and sows you are."

When he embarked on his German translation of the Bible, a project that consumed much of his life, Luther worked to render the original Greek and Hebrew sources in a recognizable German. A good translator, he declared, "must ask the mother at home, children in the street, the common man in the market, and look him in the mouth, and listen to how they speak, then translate accordingly." Luther's graceful and economic text later inspired the translators of the King James Bible.

Believing the Word alone to be an insufficient guide for ordinary people, Luther wrote dozens of *postillae*, or preaching aids, in addition to sermons, hymns, poetry, liturgies, and theological tracts. From the time he launched his reformation, in 1516, until his death in 1546, Luther wrote a treatise every other week. His writings account for an estimated 20 percent of all literature printed in Germany from 1500 to 1530.

By 1546, the year of Luther's death, more than half of Germany and four of the seven electors of the Holy Roman Empire were adherents of the Lutheran faction. A year earlier, Luther had offered a humbler assessment of his achievement. "I wished that all my books were consigned to perpetual oblivion," he wrote, "so that better ones could take their place."

George Gissing
November 22, 1857 – December 28, 1903

At 18, George Gissing was a handsome
young man, a brilliant prize-winning scholar
and linguist preparing to enter the University
of London. His life changed when he met
and fell in love with Nell, a 17-year-old
prostitute and hopeless alcoholic. In his
attempt to save her, Gissing stole money and
property. He was caught, served a month in
prison at hard labor, and was shipped to the
United States to redeem himself. He spent a
year in Massachusetts and Chicago, teaching
foreign languages and writing. When he
returned to England, he married Nell. The
marriage was a disaster, but Gissing had
found his literary subject—marriage.

"All the world is drab to him," observed the London *Times,* "save for a black spot or
two where wretchedness has led to crime."

"I exhaust myself in toil—and the public pays no heed," Gissing complained. In an
average work day, he began writing after breakfast at nine a.m. He worked until one,
ate a meal, took a walk, then at 3:30 he returned to his desk and wrote until six p.m.
He took a break, and then worked from 7:30 to about ten. Such a schedule produced
23 novels, 111 short stories, a travel book, a critical study of Dickens, and many
essays. According to his biographer John Halperin, Gisssing wrote "more than any
other 'major' Victorian novelist except Trollope."

He also found time to keep a diary. After the death of Nell, he married again. It was
another disastrous marriage. "Much misery today; grumbling, snarling, rage and
universal idiocy," he told his diary. "What a life!" He had two sons with his second
wife, but they eventually separated, and she died in a mental institution.

In his best novel, *New Grub Street,* Gissing captured the experience of literary failure
in the late-19th century, but his observations resonate into the 21st century. "Literature
nowadays is a trade," observes Jasper Milvain, a rising young journalist. "Putting
aside men of genius, who may succeed by mere cosmic force, your successful man of
letters is your skillful tradesman. He thinks first and foremost of the markets; when
one kind of goods begins to go off slackly, he is ready with something new and
appetizing."

Even Gissing, depressed, discouraged, and neurotic, could see the worth of *New Grub
Street*. "I am astonished to find how well it reads," he said. "There are savage truths
in it."

Sunday

17

Monday

18

Wyndham Lewis, b. 1882   W.S. Gilbert, b. 1836

Tuesday

19

Wednesday

20

Thomas Chatterton, b. 1752   Selma Lagerlöf, b. 1858

Thursday

21

Voltaire, b. 1694

Friday

22

André Gide, b. 1869   George Eliot, b. 1819   George Gissing, b. 1857

Saturday

23

November						
S	M	T	W	T	F	S
					1	2
3	4	5	6	7	8	9
10	11	12	13	14	15	16
17	18	19	20	21	22	23
24	25	26	27	28	29	30

November
2002

December						
S	M	T	W	T	F	S
1	2	3	4	5	6	7
8	9	10	11	12	13	14
15	16	17	18	19	20	21
22	23	24	25	26	27	28
29	30	31				

Sunday
24

Monday
25

Lope de Vega, b. 1562

Tuesday
26

Eugene Ionesco, b. 1912   Charles M. Schulz, b. 1922

Wednesday
27

Fanny Kemble, b. 1809   James Agee, b. 1909

Thursday
28

Thanksgiving Day   Dawn Powell, b. 1897   Brooks Atkinson, b. 1894

Friday
29

Chanukah begins at sunset   C.S. Lewis, b. 1898   Louisa May Alcott, b. 1832

Saturday
30

Jonathan Swift, b. 1667   Mark Twain, b. 1835   Lucy Maud Montgomery, b. 1874

November						
S	M	T	W	T	F	S
					1	2
3	4	5	6	7	8	9
10	11	12	13	14	15	16
17	18	19	20	21	22	23
24	25	26	27	28	29	30

November
2002

December						
S	M	T	W	T	F	S
1	2	3	4	5	6	7
8	9	10	11	12	13	14
15	16	17	18	19	20	21
22	23	24	25	26	27	28
29	30	31				

Charles M. Schulz
November 26, 1922 –
February 12, 2000

"Good grief, who are all these little people?" Charles Schulz once asked himself in the middle of a dark and sleepless night. "Must I live with them for the rest of my life?"

Schulz lived with Charlie Brown, Snoopy, Lucy, Linus, Woodstock, and the rest of the "Peanuts" characters for almost 50 years. Like an ancient bard, Schulz told and retold his comic epic, and there were few surprises. "All the loves in the strip are unre-quited," he said. "All the baseball games are lost; all the test scores are D-minuses; the Great Pumpkin never comes; and the football is always pulled away."

When readers wrote requesting more "happy" stories, Schulz was astonished. "You can't create humor out of happiness," he said. "Peanuts changed the comic pages forever," said cartoonist Cathy Guisewite. "It was the first strip where the characters voiced real vulnerabilities."

Schulz's own life was as bittersweet as his characters. Like Charlie Brown, he fell in love with a redhead, but when he asked her to marry him, she refused. He immortal-ized her as the "Little Red-Haired Girl." As a boy growing up in Minneapolis, Charles knew in grade school that he wanted to be a cartoonist. He graduated from high school even though he failed English and algebra and then studied art by correspondence before being drafted into the army. In World War II, he served in the 20th Armored Division as a staff sergeant. In 1949, he sold his "Li'l Folks" comic strip to United Features Syndicate. The Syndicate forced him to change the name of the strip to "Peanuts," a title he hated.

"Peanuts" spawned an industry—books, television specials and television commer-cials, a Broadway musical, toys, greeting cards, clothing, picture frames, music boxes and lunch boxes—and turned Schulz into a wealthy, and driven, man. "Drawing a daily comic strip," he said, "is not unlike having an English theme hanging over your head every day for the rest of your life." And Schulz worked every day, creating his strips on a yellow legal pad with an Esterbrook Radial pen. As he aged and his hand began to shake, he still drew all the strips himself.

On December 14, 1999, Schulz, who was suffering from colon cancer, announced that "Peanuts" would stop. "Nothing lasts forever," he said. Perhaps he was wrong. The classic "Peanuts" continues to lives in reruns. After all, as one newspaper executive pointed out, "Symphony orchestras are still playing Beethoven two hundred years after he died."

Joseph Conrad
December 3, 1857 – August 3, 1924

Although he tried to be concise, Joseph Conrad was by nature longwinded. "Conrad never wrote a true short story," said his friend and fellow novelist Ford Madox Ford. Conrad himself admitted he preferred stories of "30,000 words or so," for his desired effects "depend upon the reader *looking back* on my story as a whole."

He began writing at age 31. He wrote not in his native Polish, nor in French, in which he was fluent, but in English, which Conrad learned only in his twenties, as an emigré living in Britain. "If I had not known English," he said in 1918, "I wouldn't have written a line for print in my life." Deeply influenced by Polish, Conrad's idiosyncratic English is rife with adjectives, parallel constructions, and abstract nouns used for rhetorical effect.

He grew up Józef Teodor Konrad Korzeniowski in Polish Ukraine. His parents, both fierce nationalists, were deported to Vologda, northeast of Moscow, in 1863 after his father took part in a failed insurrection against Poland's Russian occupiers. By the time Conrad was 11, both of his parents had died from tuberculosis. A devoted uncle raised him.

A self-professed "reading boy," Conrad learned from books to lust after the sea, and at 17 he signed on with Britain's largest merchant fleet. For the next dozen or so years he sailed the world, with prolonged stays in southeast Asia and central Africa. On his return from Africa, weak with malaria and dysentery, his nerves permanently frayed, Conrad ended his nautical career. "It may be said that Africa killed Conrad the sailor and strengthened Conrad the novelist," wrote biographer Jean-Aubry. The continent inspired Conrad's most famous work, "Heart of Darkness."

He found the act of writing frustrating and slow. In his struggle to compose in English, he initially averaged just 300 words a day. "I had to work like a coal miner in his pit, quarrying all my English sentences out of a dark night," he confided. When inspiration failed him, he plummeted into depression.

In the best of his 43 works of fiction—the novels *Nostromo* and *The Secret Agent*, the novellas "The Secret Sharer" and, of course, "Heart of Darkness"—Conrad attained his highest goal. "My task…," he acknowledged, "is, by the power of the written word to make you hear, to make you feel—it is, before all, to make you see."

Sunday

1

Monday

2

Anna Comnena, b. 1083

Tuesday

3

Joseph Conrad, b. 1857

 Wednesday

4

Rainer Maria Rilke, b. 1875

Thursday

5

Ramadan ends

Friday

6

Sylvia Townsend Warner, b. 1893   Susannah Moodie, b. 1803   Ira Gershwin, b. 1896

Saturday

7

Willa Cather, b. 1873   Pearl Harbor Day

December						
S	M	T	W	T	F	S
1	2	3	4	5	6	7
8	9	10	11	12	13	14
15	16	17	18	19	20	21
22	23	24	25	26	27	28
29	30	31				

December
2002

January 2003						
S	M	T	W	T	F	S
			1	2	3	4
5	6	7	8	9	10	11
12	13	14	15	16	17	18
19	20	21	22	23	24	25
26	27	28	29	30	31	

Sunday
8

James Thurber, b. 1894

Monday
9

Tuesday
10

Emily Dickinson, b. 1830   Clarice Lispector, b. 1925   Rumer Godden, b. 1907

Wednesday
11

Thursday
12

Gustave Flaubert, b. 1821   John Osborne, b. 1929

Friday
13

Emily Carr, b. 1871   Heinrich Heine, b. 1797

Saturday
14

Shirley Jackson, b. 1919

December						
S	M	T	W	T	F	S
1	2	3	4	5	6	7
8	9	10	11	12	13	14
15	16	17	18	19	20	21
22	23	24	25	26	27	28
29	30	31				

December
2002

January 2003						
S	M	T	W	T	F	S
			1	2	3	4
5	6	7	8	9	10	11
12	13	14	15	16	17	18
19	20	21	22	23	24	25
26	27	28	29	30	31	

John Osborne
December 12, 1929—December 24, 1994

The premiere of his play *Look Back in Anger* on May 8, 1956 at the Royal Court Theater in London left audiences reeling. Strangers hugged one another, and women fainted. "I doubt if I could love anyone," wrote critic Kenneth Tynan, "who did not wish to see *Look Back in Anger.*"

John Osborne, then 26, earned the title "angry young man" for his frank portrayal of working-class life, for his anti-hero Jimmy Porter, and for his depiction of marriage as a kind of bitter class struggle.

Born into a lower-middle class family in a dismal London suburb, Osborne seems to have been bitter and angry from birth. His neighbor-hood was "full of pubs, convents, second-hand clothes shops, bagwash laundries, and pawnbrokers. Everything seemed very broken up." His father wrote advertising copy, and his mother was a barmaid. "Disappointment was oxygen to them," he said.

Sensitive because of his lowly birth, Osborne resented authority. When a master in his school hit him, he hit back. An indifferent and rebellious student, Osborne graduated from St. Michael's College, which he described as a "rather cheap boarding school." "The cinema," he said, "was my church, and my academy." From the time he was four, he saw at least two movies a week.

After working as a journalist, in 1948 he took a job as stage manager for a touring repertory theater. He became a competent repertory actor specializing in playing old men, and he began to write plays. Osborne believed that the theater could be a weapon, and his first success, *Look Back in Anger*, was just that.

His next play, *The Entertainer*, a play about Archie Rice, a seedy, music hall enter-tainer, starred Laurence Olivier as Archie, and was a huge hit. Osborne went on to write two autobiographies, screenplays, some 20 plays, including *Luther, Inadmissible Evidence,* and *A Patriot for Me.*

While his professional life was a success, his personal life was a disaster. A heavy drinker with a vitriolic temper, he married five times. He had one daughter whom he described as "a very unpleasant girl."

As disagreeable and as bitter as his anti-hero Jimmy Porter, Osborne never lost his passion, which fueled his work. "We need a new feeling as much as we need a new language," he wrote. "Out of the feeling will come the language."

Edmund Spenser
ca. 1552 – January 13, 1599

Hailed as "the Prince of Poets in his tyme," Edmund Spenser surpassed even Shakespeare in the affections of his contemporaries. At his funeral in Westminster Abbey, his body was placed "neere Chaucer," writes an historian of the period, "… all Poets carrying his body to Church, and casting their dolefull Verses, and Pens too into his grave."

For the next four centuries, Spenser's shadow loomed over English letters. "*Milton* has acknowledg'd to me that *Spencer* was his Original," reports John Dryden. Wordsworth paid tribute to "Sweet Spenser" in his *Prelude*. Byron proclaimed the Spenserian stanza "the measure most after my own heart." Keats bided the hours during his last illness by marking favorite passages in Spenser. Both Hawthorne and Melville looked to *The Faerie Queen* for examples of moral allegory and narrative.

When Spenser embarked on his unprecedented career, English literature could boast of Chaucer and the Earl of Surrey, but otherwise possessed only "bastard poets" and "poet-apes," in the words of Sir Philip Sidney, the foremost literary critic of the late16th century and an early proponent of Spenser. There was no Dante, no Petrarch or Boccaccio.

With Virgil as his model, Spenser set out to create a poetry that was distinctly English in content and form. The son of a London weaver, he was an unlikely candidate for success. He attended a tailors' school in London and then, thanks to the intervention of a teacher whom he'd impressed, Cambridge. By then, Spenser was writing poetry and had hit upon his central themes: the fragility of life and the transience of worldly matter.

He published his first work, *The Shepeardes Calender*, in 1579, a year before moving to Ireland as a government official. He remained there for years.

The Faerie Queene, the six- (originally intended as 12-) poem epic for which he is best known, appeared in 1590. Sir Walter Ralegh arranged for Spenser to present the work to Queen Elizabeth I, who was so pleased she gave Spenser a pension. The work's quasi-medieval settings, intricate metrical patterns, and romance form have enthralled countless writers—chief among them, the Romantics.

In what may be his last line of poetry, from the unfinished *Mutabilitie Cantos*, Spenser counseled, "all that moveth, doth in Change delight: / But thence-forth all shall rest eternally / With Him that is the God of Sabbaoth hight: / o that great Sabbaoth God, graunt me that Sabbaoths sight."

Sunday

15

Maxwell Anderson, b. 1888

Monday

16

Jane Austen, b. 1775   Noel Coward, b. 1899

Tuesday

17

Erskine Caldwell, b. 1903   Ford Madox Ford, b. 1873

Wednesday

18

HH. Munro (Saki), b. 1870

Thursday

19

Jean Genet, b. 1910

Friday

20

Saturday

21

Rebecca West, b. 1892   Winter Solstice, 8:15 pm EST

December						
S	M	T	W	T	F	S
1	2	3	4	5	6	7
8	9	10	11	12	13	14
15	16	17	18	19	20	21
22	23	24	25	26	27	28
29	30	31				

December
2002

January 2003						
S	M	T	W	T	F	S
			1	2	3	4
5	6	7	8	9	10	11
12	13	14	15	16	17	18
19	20	21	22	23	24	25
26	27	28	29	30	31	

Sunday
22

Monday
23

Giuseppe di Lampedusa, b. 1896

Tuesday
24

Juan Ramón Jiménez, b. 1881   Matthew Arnold, b. 1822

Wednesday
25

Christmas Day   Carlos Castaneda, b. 1931   Quentin Crisp, b. 1908

Thursday
26

Boxing Day (Canada, U.K.)
Kwanzaa   Jean Toomer, b. 1894   Henry Miller, b. 1891

Friday
27

Saturday
28

December						
S	M	T	W	T	F	S
1	2	3	4	5	6	7
8	9	10	11	12	13	14
15	16	17	18	19	20	21
22	23	24	25	26	27	28
29	30	31				

December
2002

January 2003						
S	M	T	W	T	F	S
			1	2	3	4
5	6	7	8	9	10	11
12	13	14	15	16	17	18
19	20	21	22	23	24	25
26	27	28	29	30	31	

Quentin Crisp
December 25, 1908 –
November 21, 1999

Wags called him "one of
the great stately homos of
England." Author of twelve
books and a one-man show,
Crisp simply said that he was
"in the profession of being."

He grew up in a London suburb
as plain Dennis Pratt, the son of
a lawyer and a former governess. Tormented by a homopho-
bic society, he decided to celebrate his differences and dedicate his life to "making the
existence of homosexuality abundantly clear to the world's aborigines."

He worked for a time as an artist's model, an actor, a commercial artist, and a critic.
But with the publication of his autobiography, *The Naked Civil Servant*, in 1968, it
was clear that he was a gifted writer, witty, shocking, sometimes absurd, always
candid, and often profound.

In 1977, when he was 69, he moved from England to Manhattan's Lower East Side
and established himself in a one-room apartment on Third Street. A flamboyant dandy
in a black fedora, colorful scarves, and eyeshadow, he lived unmolested amid "drug
dealers, pimps, derelicts, Hell's Angels and all manner of low life." In 1978, he starred
in a one-man show, *An Evening with Quentin Crisp,* which earned a special Drama
Desk Award, and he became a celebrity. "In the rest of the world, fame is something
that happens to you," he said, "but in the United States it is something you do."

With panache and unbelievable energy for a man his age, Crisp went into the fame
business. He claimed to live on peanuts and champagne and never refused an invitation to a party or an interview. Television was "the survival of the glibbest," he
quipped. He accepted countless speaking engagements around the country. "Los
Angeles is New York lying down," he said. He delighted audiences because he
believed that "no one is boring who is willing to tell the truth about himself."

After he played Queen Elizabeth I in the 1993 film *Orlando,* when his Village
neighbors spotted him on the street they bowed and kissed his hand. Once called one
of the wittiest men alive, Crisp was also one of the most lovable.

He died at 90 in Manchester, England, the day before his one-man show was to open.
Crisp drew out the universal, wrote critic Richard Eder, "gaiety—in the original sense
of the word…and themes common to all of us: the need for courage and individuality,
and the ground of tragedy on which they are exercised."

Paul Bowles
December 30, 1910 – November 18, 1999

In an interview in 1981, Paul Bowles said, "Everyone is isolated from everyone else." A poet, short-story writer, novelist, composer, translator, he never sought fame, but he did touch lives, particularly other writers like Truman Capote, Tennessee Williams, Christopher Isherwood, and Allen Ginsberg.

Bowles's sense of isolation stemmed from his youth growing up in Queens, New York. An only child, he was haunted by a family legend that echoed the plot of d'Annunzio's novel, *The Innocent*. According to the family story, Bowles's father took off his baby son's clothes, put him in a basket, and placed him outside on a windowsill during a snowstorm to die. The boy survived the exposure as well as his middle-class upbringing and escaped into music and literature. After briefly attending the University of Virginia, he fled to Paris, where he met Gertrude Stein, Jean Cocteau and André Gide.

He hated the wintry cold of Paris, and Alice Toklas suggested that he try Morocco. In 1931, he moved to Tangier for a time before returning to New York. During the 1930s and 1940s, Bowles concentrated on musical composition, writing scores for seven plays, including *The Glass Menagerie*. Virgil Thomson called Bowles's songs enchanting. "The texts fit their tunes like a peach in its skin," he said. After Bowles married writer Jane Auer, though, he was inspired by her writing and began to write as well.

When the "magic city" of Tangier appeared to him in a dream, he moved there permanently in 1947. Gertrude Stein had praised his descriptions in his early work, and in his best-selling novel, *The Sheltering Sky* (1949), he described the Sahara. "During the middle of the day it was no longer the sun alone that persecuted from above—the entire sky was like a metal dome grown white with heat. The merciless light pushed down from all directions; the sun was the whole sky."

Just as Bowles had learned from an earlier generation of writers, a new generation flocked to Tangier to meet him. "If you discover you're affecting other people," Bowles once said, "you have to stop doing whatever you're doing." Still, he was gracious if somewhat distant with the young people who sought him out. "It was my good fortune," poet Daniel Halpern wrote, "to have encountered Paul and, second-hand, the life he had lived—an entire world I partly inherited through his past."

Sunday
29

Monday
30

Paul Bowles, b. 1910   *Rudyard Kipling, b. 1865*

Tuesday
31

Wednesday
1

Isaac Asimov, b. 1920   *Catherine Drinker Bowen, b. 1897*   New Year's Day

 Thursday
2

Friday
3

Saturday
4

December						
S	M	T	W	T	F	S
1	2	3	4	5	6	7
8	9	10	11	12	13	14
15	16	17	18	19	20	21
22	23	24	25	26	27	28
29	30	31				

December 2002/
January 2003

January 2003						
S	M	T	W	T	F	S
			1	2	3	4
5	6	7	8	9	10	11
12	13	14	15	16	17	18
19	20	21	22	23	24	25
26	27	28	29	30	31	

Selected Sources

"Paul Bowles, Elusive Composer and Author Known for 'Sheltering Sky,' Dies at 88," by Mel Gussow. *The New York Times*, November 19, 1999. B14.

Bagnold, Enid. *Enid Bagnold's Autobiography*. Boston: Little, Brown, 1969.

Beerbohm, Max. *Letters of Max Beerbohm 1892–1956*. Ed. Rupert Hart-Davis. New York: W.W. Norton, 1989.

Benedetti, Jean. *Stanislavski*. New York: Routledge, 1988.

Bloom, Harold, ed. *Ralph Ellison. Modern Critical Views*. New York: Chelsea House, 1986.

Broner, E.M. "Meridel LeSueur, 1900–1996." *The Nation*. February 17, 1997.

Bruccoli, Matthew. *The O'Hara Concern. A Biography of John O'Hara*. New York: Random House, 1975.

Busby, Mark. *Ralph Ellison*. Boston: Twayne, 1991.

Callahan, John. "American Culture Is of a Whole: From the Letters of Ralph Ellison." *New Republic*. March 1, 1999.

Cecil, David. *Max. A Biography*. Boston: Houghton Mifflin, 1965.

Charlton, James. *Fighting Words. Writers Lambast Other Writers—from Aristotle to Anne Rice*. James Charlton, ed. Chapel Hill, North Carolina: Algonquin Books, 1994.

Claiborne, Craig. *A Feast Made for Laughter*. Garden City, New York: Doubleday, 1982.

Crisp, Quentin. *Resident Alien. The New York Diaries*. Los Angeles: Alyson Books, 1996.

David, Deirdre. *Intellectual Women and Victorian Patriarchy*. Ithaca, New York: Cornell University Press, 1987.

David, James Herbert. *Fénelon*. Boston: Twayne, 1979.

Duncan, Isadora. *My Life*. New York: Liveright, 1995.

Eisenberg, Lee. "He's Tiger Woods and You're Not." *New York Times Book Review*. August 17, 1997.

Ellis, Roger. *Peter Weiss in Exile. A Critical Study of His Works*. Ann Arbor, Michigan: UMI Research Press, 1987.

Ellison, Ralph. *Going into the Territory*. New York: Random House, 1986.

Fadiman, Clifton, and John S. Major. *The New Lifetime Reading Plan*. New York: HarperCollins, 1997.

Falb, Lewis W. *Jean Anouilh*. New York: Frederick Ungar, 1977.

Fazia, Alba Della. *Jean Anouilh*. New York: Twayne, 1969.

Frenzel, Ivo. *Friedrich Nietzsche*. New York: Pegasus, 1967.

Gracián, Baltasar. *The Art of Worldly Wisdom*. Trans. Christopher Maurer. New York: Doubleday/Currency, 1991.

Hallett, Richard. *Isaac Babel*. New York: Frederick Ungar, 1973.

Halperin, John. *Gissing. A Life in Books*. Oxford: Oxford University Press, 1987.

Heller, Joseph. *Now and Then. From Coney Island to Here*. New York, Knopf, 1998.

Hiney, Tom. *Raymond Chandler*. New York: Atlantic Monthly Press, 1997.

Hirsch, Edward. "Octavio Paz: In Defense of Poetry." *New York Times Book Review*. June 7, 1998.

Hirsch, Edward. "On Donald Barthelme." *TriQuarterly*. Winter 96/97, Issue 98.

Johnson, Walter. *August Strindberg*. Boston: Twayne, 1976.

Kilgour, Maggie. *The Rise of the Gothic Novel*. London and New York: Routledge, 1995.

Lang, Paul Henry. *The Experience of Opera*. New York: Norton, 1971.

Marsh, Ngaio. *Black Beech and Honey-dew*. Boston: Little, Brown, 1965.

Meyer, Michael. *Ibsen. A Biography*. Garden City, New York: Doubleday, 1971.

Mitford, Jessica. *A Fine Old Conflict*. New York: Knopf, 1977.

Nicholls, Richard. "Iris Murdoch, Novelist and Philosopher, Is Dead." *New York Times*. February 9, 1999.

Osborne, John. *A Better Class of Person*. New York: Dutton, 1981.

Punter, David, ed. *A Companion to the Gothic*. Malden, Massachusetts: Blackwell Publishers, 2000.

Sade, Marquis de. *Justine*. New York: Castle Books, 1964.

Schleuning, Neala. *America: Song We Sang without Knowing. The Life and Ideas of Meridel LeSueur*. Mankato, Minn.: Little Red Hen Press, 1983.

Severo, Richard. "Clifton Fadiman, a Wordsmith Known for His Encyclopedic Knowledge, Is Dead at 95." *New York Times*. June 21, 1999.

Solomon, Robert C. and Higgins, Kathleen M. *What Nietzsche Really Said*. New York: Schocken, 2000.

St. Clair, William. *The Godwins and The Shelleys*. New York: W.W. Norton, 1989.

Smith, D. Howard. *Confucius*. London: Temple Smith, 1973.

Stanislavski, Constantin. *My Life In Art*. New York: Routledge, 1952.

Steegmuller, Francis. *A Woman, A Man, and Two Kingdoms. The Story of Madame d'Épinay and the Abbé Galiani*. New York: Knopf, 1991.

Varma, Devendra P. *The Gothic Flame*. Metuchen, N.J. and London: Scarecrow Press, 1987.

Weidmann, Paul. "Marquis de Sade: Six Letters from Prison..." *Chicago Review*. 1993, Vol. 39, Issue 2.

Weisstein, Ulrich. *The Essence of Opera*. New York: Norton, 1964.

Wright, David. *Roy Campbell*. London: Longmans, Green, 1961.

Photo and Illustration Credits

Jean Anouilh	©Bettmann/CORBIS
Max Beerbohm	Culver Pictures
Paul Bowles	©AFP/CORBIS
Roy Campbell	©Hulton-Deutsch Collection/CORBIS
Raymond Chandler	©Bettmann/CORBIS
Joseph Conrad	Library of Congress: A.L. Coburn, artist, 1916
Quentin Crisp	©Bettmann/CORBIS
Mme. d'Épinay	Culver Pictures
Marquis de Sade	Culver Pictures
Isadora Duncan	Courtesy Leslie Stainton
Ralph Ellison	©Bettmann/CORBIS
Clifton Fadiman	© J. Ross Baughman/Courtesy Anne Fadiman
François Fénelon	Culver Pictures
George Gissing	Culver Pictures
William Godwin	Culver Pictures
Golf	Library of Congres: G.D. Armour, artist, 1906
Rider H. Haggard	Culver Pictures
Sarah Josepha Hale	Culver Pictures
Joseph Heller	© Reuters Newsmedia Inc./CORBIS
T.E. Lawrence	Culver Pictures
Meridel LeSueur	© Freda Leinwand
Compton MacKenzie	Library of Congress: A.L. Coburn, artist, 1914
Ngaio Marsh	©Hulton-Deutsch Collection/CORBIS
Harriet Martineau	Culver Pictures
Jessica Mitford	UPI
Eugenio Montale	©Studio Patellani/CORBIS
Friedrich Nietzsche	Culver Pictures
John Osborne	©Hulton-Deutsch Collection/CORBIS
Octavio Paz	©Bettmann/CORBIS
Charles Schulz	AP/Wide World Photos
Constantin Stanislavski	Culver Pictures
August Strindberg	Culver Pictures
Peter Weiss	© Renate von Mangoldt (LCB), courtesy Suhrkamp Verlag
Marguerite Young	©LaVerne Harrell Clark, courtesy Dalkey Archives

Index

About the Authors

The authors of *On Writers and Writing* are both biographers.
Helen Sheehy is the author of *Margo: The Life and Theatre of
Margo Jones* (Southern Methodist University Press, 1989) and *Eva
Le Gallienne* (Alfred A. Knopf, 1996). She is currently working on
a biography of Eleonora Duse for Knopf. A resident of Connecti-
cut, Sheehy has written a theater textbook, a number of articles and
essays, and has taught theater for more than twenty-five years.

Leslie Stainton lives in Michigan. She is the author of *Lorca:
A Dream of Life* (Bloomsbury, 1998; Farrar, Straus and Giroux,
1999). Her articles and essays have appeared in various newspapers
and periodicals including *The New York Times*, *The Washington
Post*, and *American Theatre* magazine.